The Augmented Workforce

How Artificial Intelligence, Augmented Reality, and 5G
Will Impact Every Dollar You Make

Cathy Hackl and John Buzzell

Renown Publishing
www.renownpublishing.com

The Augmented Workforce / Cathy Hackl and John Buzzell
www.TheAugmentedWorkforce.com

ISBN-13: 978-1-952602-39-9

For those who see the possibilities before they become obvious and believe in their capacity to create a better future. I dedicated this book to my children and to all the women in tech who have struggled within this industry. I aspire to be a beacon of hope, change, and of what's possible.
—Cathy Hackl

To my parents, who fostered my lifelong love of technology; to my lovely wife ,who has put up with it so patiently; and to my children, who continually inspire me to share it.
—John Buzzell

CONTENTS

Foreword by Brian Solis

This Is the Virtual Sign You've Been Waiting For

Imagine you're in the "Metaverse."[1] It's an incredible escape from the limitations of reality, as you explore new worlds, meet new people, and indulge in mind-bending experiences. You become someone else, the person you always felt you were meant to be. You feel alive and empowered to do so much more than you can accomplish when you unplug. You're surrounded by amazing things and people you would never have encountered or met, otherwise.

This is more than an escape. It's the Metaverse. To you and millions of others, it's a real world where you feel relevant, part of a community that's exploring a new frontier. This. Is. What. Matters.

Avatars in these virtual worlds represent real human beings, and they're paving the way for more than personal entertainment. They're broadening their horizons, learning how to connect, learn, and express themselves in new ways while pushing the boundaries of reality itself. For those paying attention, our adventures in immersive realities are evolving how we communicate, connect, work, discover, and share. And when you come back to the real world, you start to question why it is you have to stop. "Why aren't these experiences part of everyday life?" you ask yourself.

Well, that's just how the world works, isn't it?

The truth is that the way the world works today was imagined in a time that no longer exists.

Again: This. Is. What. Matters.

The systems originally built for basically all that we do today are failing. As society advances, dated infrastructure, mindsets, and metrics, not technology, hinder progress.

The future of how we live and work, our relationship with innovation, and our very construct for productivity and engagement, are overdue for a digital, physical, and hybrid renaissance. Who are our artists to imagine and create the future? Who are the da Vincis, Michelangelos, Raphaels, or Donatellos of our time?

The answer is: you.

That's why you're reading this. It's also why Cathy and John wrote this book. You are, they are, we are all curious. We're dreamers. We're geeks. We believe that something greater lies ahead, because we're already experiencing wonders in our personal lives: Artificial Intelligence. Augmented reality. Immersive audio. Virtual reality. 5G.

Why bring these experiences, our ideas, and our passions together to reimagine the future of work, business, engagement, and experiences? Someone has to. So, why can't it be you? The future needs you to imagine forward— to engineer next-generation relationships between people, between screens and machines, and between virtual and real-world experiences. You can play a role in shaping the future you want to *see*.

As much as we want to forget it, 2020 was a pivotal year for us. Through disruption and chaos, we found a new way forward. We learned that we are more capable, resilient, and inventive than we previously gave ourselves credit for. But this isn't the last disruption we'll face. Another pandemic, climate change, social transformation, political shifts, and the unknown lie ahead. We're also in the throes of the Fourth Industrial Revolution ("4IR"), which is completely reshaping, well, everything.

Think about it. If not now, when? If not you, then who?

Just because the way we live or work has "always been done this way" doesn't mean that it is the best way or the only way forward. The 4IR is already forcing human workers to reskill and to reconnect with soft (although really hard) skills including creativity, critical thinking, empathy, problem solving, initiative, and active learning.

What we see and do can be augmented to bring the Metaverse to life in our work. The 4IR can power more incredible experiences that we haven't yet seen, or even imagined. That's why you play a more important role than you may think. You have an opportunity to envision the future, today. You can be the architect, the engineer—the builder of immersive, productive, and fantastical digital and hybrid experiences.

Look, I get it. It's easy to find every reason why we can't change the rules, throw caution to the wind, or immerse ourselves in something new and different without checking certain boxes first.

But change happens, with or without us. Change also happens to us or because of us. It really is a choice.

The same old thinking and beliefs will never change the world. As the saying goes, "Insanity is doing the same thing over and over again, but expecting different results." I believe that *you believe* the world would be a better place because of your ideas.

Thank you for coming along on this journey. You're in good hands with Cathy and John. Together, you'll not only transform how you work and live, but you'll also make a dent in the universe. You'll inspire remarkable changes in the design of how people, things, and places co-exist, communicate, and come to life. I can't wait.

Introduction by Cathy Hackl

I've had a machine implanted into my body. After some complications from a surgery, a doctor put a machine inside me to help me heal faster.

This machine and I were essentially one. I ate, worked, and slept with it. Whenever my battery got low, I'd plug "myself" in.

Once I even said to my kids, "Mommy can't help you right now. She's recharging."

"Are you a cyborg now?" my son asked.

"Mommy's more like a Tesla," I joked, realizing that cyborgs don't have to be plugged in every few hours.

A few years earlier, a friend of mine had a similarly life-changing moment with technology. One day, at my daughter's soccer game, I ran into Paula, a close friend I hadn't seen in a while—and she was walking! I was astounded. A former tennis champion, Paula was suddenly disabled a few years ago by a mysterious illness. She couldn't even lift one of her kids. And here she was! Walking!

Little metal strut-like things were strapped on her legs. Long story short, a doctor had hooked her up with a hybrid prosthetic-orthotic device. The hybrid prosthetic-orthotic looked like a mix between a walking boot and a prosthetic limb. Paula wore it on her leg and foot. The design stores energy so each step advances Paula forward. The device works around an injury that's not tolerant of movement through its dynamic design.[2] Watching my previously paralyzed friend strolling around, I thought, *Now that's human augmentation. It isn't*

*androids in a bad Hollywood movie taking over the planet.
It's a mother going to her daughter's soccer game.*

When it comes to human augmentation, some naysayers only dwell on potential negatives. As a futurist, I'm always analyzing the full spectrum of possibilities. But I focus more on the possible and plausible. To me, human augmentation—and everything related to artificial intelligence and augmented reality—has the power to improve and transform the workplace as much as the Industrial Revolution did centuries ago. And yet our current Technological Revolution won't just enhance our physical abilities. It will also augment our cognitive capacity.

I'm speaking from experience.

As a futurist, I live five to ten years into the future and I get to play with the coolest tech before it's publicly released. But these experiences—myself being a living Tesla and seeing Paula walk—reminded me of how incredibly lucky we all are to be living in a time when emerging tech can make our lives better.

And it's not just our personal lives that will be enhanced. Our workplaces will be transformed, too.

An augmented workforce is already changing the world and revolutionizing how we do business—smart farming, environmental monitoring, resilient cities, wearable tech, interactive training, and much more.

But what will this all mean for us as workers? What does it mean for the future of the workplace? What are the possibilities? What are the limitations and opportunities? A belief inspired this book—the belief that technology will make this a better world for everyone.

Other business disruptions, like the COVID-19 pandemic, are moving a whole new segment of the workforce to working from home. While some organizations see the pandemic as a challenge, for others it's an opportunity for greater efficiency, a chance to modernize. We live an analog life, but for many people, we already work in the digital and virtual.

Part I:
Welcome to the Future, Again

CHAPTER ONE

Dearly Disrupted

We are living through a period of rapid change, possibly beyond society's capacity to keep up. There's an unprecedented acceleration and convergence of technology. It's rampant and widespread. Various emerging technologies, such as artificial intelligence (AI), augmented reality (AR), virtual reality (VR), and 5G, along with dozens of devices that work together (Internet of Things), have helped to create an environment in which new inventions, possibilities, and learning curves change weekly.

According to Peter Diamandis and Steven Kotler, authors of *The Future Is Faster Than You Think*, "Moore's Law is the reason the smartphone in your pocket is a thousand times smaller, a thousand times cheaper, and a million times more powerful than a supercomputer from the 1970s. In 2023 the average thousand-dollar laptop will have the same computing power as a human brain (roughly 10^{16} cycles per second). Twenty-five years after that, that same average laptop will have the power of all the human brains currently on Earth."[3] That's rampant, exponential acceleration.

Rampant Acceleration

In the past, there was a slow evolution of technology, which gave people time to adapt. In the decade to come, it will feel more like the Cambrian Explosion—an event over 500 million years ago when most living things burst into being. For instance, radio preceded the advent of the television by decades, which trained people to go to a device for news and entertainment. Mainstream cell phones predated the smartphone's popularity by thirty years and slowly changed how we interact and work. The Internet was prevalent for ten years before mobile apps were popularized and changed how we consumed and processed information. These gradual changes, one on top of the other, made for a smooth transition from a typical household living in the 1950s to a family living in the 2000s. How many people today use a smartphone, laptop, ebook, and tablet multiple times a day? This would've been unthinkable in 1950. But the change was gradual and maneuverable.

Make no mistake—technology is evolving, as is our relationship with it. In the first phase of the Internet, we connected information. A person could search the web using a search engine, send a document via email, and use all this new information in novel ways. The second phase of the Internet connected people. Facebook and Twitter created a social media revolution, conceivably connecting one person with millions of other people in ways that were unthinkable in the past (e.g., think of a president's or movie star's Twitter feed). And in the third phase (which we're entering), the Internet is connecting people, places, and things in a more dynamic and amplified way.

The Internet of Things is amplifying the concept of location and the concept of merging our digital and physical lives. It's gradually impacting more of how we live, work, and play. A union of digital and physical realities, already seamlessly affecting many areas of our lives. From an acceleration technology standpoint, we're seeing an even greater change than what we've seen in the past—and at a faster pace. The combined rate and scale of change is causing exponential acceleration.

Diamandis and Kotler, again in *The Future Is Faster than You Think*, wrote, "In the next decade, we'll experience more progress than in the past 100 years." They explain:

> *We've been living through a time of constantly accelerating technological capabilities. We're living in a world of increasing, exponentially growing computational power. Technology is always on, always available, and we're now moving into the quantum computing era— these exponential technologies are enabling artificial intelligence, robotics, 3D printing, synthetic biology, augmented reality, blockchain and allowing these technologies to converge, creating new business models. It's the convergence of these technologies that creates waves on top of waves of capability, which will change our world—every industry—our economy, our government, our health, our families. Everything is beginning to change.[4]*

If you think that is a great deal to consider, Diamandis and Kotler also predict that meta-intelligence (i.e., when humans merge with technology), will take place in less than twenty years. We will be able to connect our brains with the Cloud.[5] The accumulation of AI, AR, 5G, and IoT, plus related technologies such as crypto/blockchain and extended reality (XR) may have snuck up on us, but we can adapt and catch up.

Business Disruption

Businesses are constantly on the lookout for things that decrease time, cost, and increase value. That's why businesses are one of the main drivers of technology. Manufacturers equip operators with augmented reality devices. Instead of reading a paper manual or asking another person for help, AR glasses teach operators where to go for parts or how to fix equipment. Connected sensors on hardhats monitor workers' location and notify them of dangers or other equipment.

In the restaurant industry, line cooks work alongside robot arms equipped with different appendages like hamburger flippers or deep fry baskets. Even marketing teams have to evolve as they work with digital influencers (CGI people who pose with sponsored clothing or gear).

We're used to working side-by-side with devices that we believe are safe, and doing that saves us time. For instance, many families have a robotic vacuum cleaner, and they don't think twice about it. Warehouses use robots to fetch and store packages. Tye Brady, Amazon Robotics' chief technologist, said, "The efficiencies we gain from our associates and robotics working together harmoniously—what I like to call a symphony of humans and machines working together—allows us to pass along a lower cost to our customer."[6] As these "cobots" (robot co-workers or collaborative robots) become prevalent, it's likely that our interaction in the home with Alexa, Siri, or Roomba, will have conditioned us to be accepting of our new digital co-workers.

Conferences are disrupted by virtual reality. In 2018, Cathy spoke at Lethbridge College's Merging Realities, the first conference hosted in virtual reality. Over three hundred people registered for the event.[7] People outfitted their avatars in business attire. At the end of the keynote, MetaVRse CEO Alan Smithson asked everyone to throw digital confetti into the air.

Virtual reality reduces costs to participants since hosts do not have to rent out large convention centers. It also opens the doors to even more participants since people aren't held back by physical constraints. Vendors create 3D booths to upload into the lobby. "Instead of handing out pens and candy, they can give away free credits to their product or services, something that would actually be more beneficial since it brings potential customers right to their website instead of a pen they'll forget in a desk drawer," said Lily Snyder, digital technologist. "Vendors who pay a premium can have a whole virtual experience of their product or service in action for participants to take part in."

Since then virtual reality conferences like Enablers of Tomorrow, Women in XR Venture Fund Pitch Showcase, and Educators in VR Summit are all examples of VR disrupting business. Public speakers better engage with audiences in "nonlinear conversations."[8] Talking points, instead of planned slides, allow the audience to more easily move from topic to topic based on their interest. VR provides subject material on an as-needed basis instead of going from slide to slide. Immersive environments like virtual and augmented reality and holographic telepresence make more sense than ever. Virtual reality is data-rich, providing a whole new level to the conference experience.

At the time of writing this book, companies are getting rid of their corporate headquarters, opting to stay remote even after the pandemic subsides. Kara Swisher stated that Zoom's shares rose 60 percent in the month of February 2020 as employees embarked on a litany of Zoom meetings from home.[9] One managing director at Accenture asked her team to buy Oculus Quests headsets so they could meet virtually for daily tasks.[10] In the past she had only used VR for specific training modules or client needs but after a few weeks using VR with her team she noticed "group energy and sense of camaraderie are better than with any other mode of communication."

A training manager at Nestle Purina thinks using VR will "help the company recruit a more technically fluent workforce in the future."[11] Nestle Purina uses virtual reality to build out shelf ideas and category concepts. VR lowers the risk for employees who build live tests. It also accelerates time to market because of the shared vision customers and employees virtually walk through together. "Instead of showing them PowerPoint after PowerPoint or showing them a demo that might not be to scale, we're able to use the virtual reality technology in ways that offer customized solutions and allow us to make changes over and over and over again,"[12] said Kenny Endermuhle, Senior Manager of Retail Innovation Strategy at Nestlé Purina.

Months into the 2020 coronavirus pandemic, a local chapter of the Construction Financial Management Association conducted their monthly meeting in virtual reality. The virtual reality boardroom was what the chapter needed after burnout from "zoom fatigue."[13] Experiencing the immersion of virtual reality once inspired construction firms in the meeting to investigate other opportunities for augmented and mixed reality.

The companies that can provide tools to work from home are the ones experiencing growth and profits. Yet, even with this data, some companies decided not to hold virtual conferences. In early and mid-2020, they canceled or postponed previously scheduled (physical) conferences, even across tech-forward industries like telecommunications, entertainment, and social networking. Their failure to adapt cost them business.

Social Disruption

The Internet and mobile technology changed how we communicate as human beings. Generation Z (a.k.a., the iGeneration) make and break friendships on social media, never confronting each other in real life. Families are divided online by algorithms that feed them one-sided articles, making Thanksgiving dinner a battle of "Fake News." The Internet, with its promise of opening world views, now seems to close them. From a social standpoint, the convergence of technologies will continue to change how we interact with family members, friends, and co-workers. In under ten years, people will be able to experience a volumetric or holographic (3D visual) representation of a friend or family member in front of them. They'll be able to have a conversation with someone as if they were sitting in the same room, though thousands of miles apart.

At Magic Leap, Cathy worked with an amazing team of software developers on spatial computing, which Simon Greenwold defines as "human interaction with a machine in which the machine retains and manipulates referents to real objects and spaces."[14] The team created a mixed reality chessboard and the ability to play against a live 3D opponent. One chess player was on the first floor, and the other was on the second floor. They saw each other as holographic images and could see each other's moves as they played on the virtual chessboard. Companies like Spatial, Rec Room, AlcoveVR, VR chat, and Galaxity are among the spatial computing companies altering the way we work and play from a social standpoint. These social VR apps change the way we share experiences, how we share photos of our vacations, and how we relate to people because we're interacting in a 3D space and experiencing the same presence as in real life.

If given a choice, most students would likely rather have a volumetric display of Abraham Lincoln giving a speech than read about it or watch a video representation of it. Holograms have something 2D videos don't: presence. When people interact with a volumetric video, they have the experience that they are there with that person, and they experience emotion and memory that comes from physical interaction.

Internet dating will change dramatically when people do not have to guess whether a flat picture represents the person accurately since they will have a holographic display of the person right in front of them that may be harder to manipulate. Instead of having quarantine-safe first dates on Skype, potential couples can date via volumetric video. Someone who may come across as boring or distant on video can be themselves by moving around as a hologram. And if the date isn't working out? Simply shut off the stream.

Maybe someone tested positive for an asymptomatic version of a virus. They want to go dancing but don't want to get anyone sick. Dance clubs will enable people to join the dance floor where they'll be a holographic presence for others to see and to experience the club themselves using VR. The possibilities are endless.

Golf and country clubs are already being reimagined with virtual reality. Ready Player Golf re-envisions a golf outing in virtual reality. Friends join in VR to play a few holes. Colleagues or business partners can join in for a virtual game and talk business. Charities like Doctors Without Borders have taken advantage of the social aspect of VR in Ready Player Golf. RPG generated $12,300 from 78 donors and sponsors.[15]

We may be physical creatures, but we now have digital personas as well. These existences—online and offline, physical and digital—are slowly merging. That doesn't mean that future generations will always represent themselves as their physical persona in the digital world. They can choose to be the color purple, a dinosaur, or a superhero—or all three! In the future, people will choose to be whatever they want to be because they're a lot more fluid in their concept of identity. And that will transcend even further in the future.

For instance, Facebook has created a VR world called Facebook Horizon, which it describes as a "social experience where you can explore, play, and create with others in VR."[16] Cathy was an early beta tester of Facebook Horizon. She was one of the first people to livestream from inside Horizon and show the world what it looks like. In Horizon people are represented by avatars that look like themselves as their Horizon avatar is linked to their Facebook profile. People can play games, but more interestingly create worlds that their friends can explore. Here lies the possibility for monetizing digital goods within Facebook, making virtual living a profitable one. Facebook Horizon is monitored by real Facebook employees (represented as avatars) to avoid some of the social pitfalls that can effect people in VR.

While Facebook essentially requires you to be "you" in VR, other virtual realities allow more freedom where a boy might appear as the wizard Gandalf, or an older woman may appear as Iron Man. These virtual realities are interesting because they allow people to experience a completely different life. But, anonymity is not without consequences. Social VR is like the early days of the Internet. People met in chat rooms and talked to strangers; there were no online rules of etiquette.[17] In some social VR platforms, people "sensory bomb" others who are new to VR, causing them confusion without a chance to escape or set boundaries. In the workforce, etiquette and social harassment guidelines will need to be put in place before deploying VR. People will find significance and purpose in the virtual world, which will change how they relate to each other in the physical world. We anticipate seeing job ads in the future for people who can work seamlessly between digital and physical realities. We think this way because job titles like "hologram stylist" exist today. Hologram stylists at Metastage work with people to prepare them for volumetric video capture. They pick clothes to wear and how a person's hair should best be worn so that it is fully captured in 3D. Fashion brands like Gucci are already turning to digital only clothing and accessories. Virtual couture designers make digital fashion first, in the form of filters or 3D assets. As we depend on AI robots, like Amazon Alexa or Siri, they will become gatekeepers. Business-to-Robot-Consumer (B2R2C) marketing managers will reach customers through robots. No matter how we communicate, we expect AR, VR, AI, and 5G to have an impact.

Entertainment Disruption

Hollywood is shifting to more immersive content—not just for viewers but also during production. In 2016, director Jon Favreau started experimenting with VR through a film called *Gnomes & Goblins*. He took what he learned and applied them to his remakes of *The Jungle Book* and *The Lion King*.

Traditionally, for a blend of live-action and animated films, the actors speak into a microphone while standing up, remaining stationary when recording their lines. Instead of utilizing the traditional route, Favreau had the performers act together in a live space so that he could capture their movements and their facial expressions. He then incorporated that into the animation. Favreau also had people act using VR so that they could see themselves as a lion, hyena, or a warthog. The crew joined them in VR too. This changed how people performed because they were able to see themselves as the animated character and were able to interact in a digital space. If you had to play a lion, would you rather stand still at a

microphone or see yourself as a lion in VR? Peter Rubin
from *Wired* wrote:

> The Lion King *was filmed entirely in virtual reality (well,*
> *save a single photographed shot). All the locations you*
> *know from the original—Pride Rock, the elephant*
> *graveyard, Rafiki's Ancient Tree—exist, but not as*
> *practical sets or files confined to an animator's computer.*
> *They live inside a kind of filmmaking video-game as 360-*
> *degree virtual environments, full of digitized animals,*
> *around which Favreau and his crew could roam. Headsets*
> *on, filmmakers had access to all the tools of the trade, just*
> *in virtual form.*[18]

We believe this will lead to a transition from storytelling, where we're passive recipients of information to "story-living," where we're active participants in the story with agency—a capacity to act independently. The ultimate way to experience this will be in an artificial reality like VR. Of course, this isn't completely new. There have been branching narrative concepts in the past, blending "choose your own adventure," with certain digital technologies. In approximately five years from now, there will be another shift from "story living" to "story doing" (similar to AR) where the person is part of the story. Think of a supercharged version of *Pokémon GO*. The previously passive audience will now be active, leading to improvements in engagement and entertainment. The increased use of interactive storytelling techniques will blur the lines between mediums. Watching a pitched medieval battle on TV? Pick up the controller (or your VR headset!) and help turn the tide. This transformative experience is coming soon to a screen near you.

"Mom, Be Nice to Alexa"

As devices become more ubiquitous in our lives, attitudes and views of these devices are shifting. Our phones are always on, our email is a tap away, and we humans are learning to work with machines. Not only might we have a machine as a co-worker, but we've also adopted a plethora of technologies in the home. We're learning about how our personal and work lives integrate as offices sneak home with us in our smartphones. Instead of seeing a work-life balance, we believe it's a circle. For instance, Jeff Bezos revealed that the relationship between his career and personal life is reciprocal, and that he doesn't compartmentalize the two like most people do. He stated, "I get asked about work-life balance all the time. And my view is, that's a debilitating phrase because it implies there's a strict trade-off. It actually is a circle. It's not a balance."[19]

This may be why younger generations view devices differently than older ones. Cathy sees her Amazon Alexa as a gadget. Her children experience Alexa more like a digital friend. Case in point, if Cathy speaks to Alexa in a direct or authoritative tone because the virtual assistant isn't understanding her, then her son will say, "Mom, be nice to Alexa." Because children view Alexa as a digital companion, they will be more likely to embrace robots or cobots in the future.

Internet of Everything

Starting as recently as 1999, we've called the community of networked devices the "Internet of things" (IoT). This title is already becoming outdated, and quickly. Because of the rapid expansion of connected persons, places, and things, always-on connectivity, data is continuously being transmitted from our phones, computers, cars, and locations, as well as a network of countless other devices and sensors. Our purchases, our exercise routines, web-browsing, thermostat habits, and *much* more are being monitored, analyzed, and monetized. Devices and sensors have created a web of information that governments and companies can use. This is why data has been called "the new oil." However, this analogy is too crude—pun intended—because oil is a finite resource, whereas new data is being created every second around the world. Billions of devices are now interconnected through the Internet with AI, analyzing data to increase efficiency, and experts utilizing this data to improve products, services, and new technologies. However, it's not just things that are being connected. People (e.g. texting), places (e.g. teleconferencing), and actions (e.g. shopping) are being constantly connected too. Thus, the Internet of *Everything* might be a better label.

Our thermostats, door-cams, light switches, fridges, smartwatches, and smart TVs are all linked on the same network and can be controlled by a few apps. Not to mention a dozen sensors that are controlled by our home security system, all connected and managed on our devices—all thanks to the Internet. But, this is just in the home.

The healthcare industry uses IoT by connecting medical devices and healthcare services for health-related purposes and analysis. The same could be said about manufacturing, agriculture, or transportation. Communications, control, and information processing are managed through a single network. Self-driving cars monitor hundreds of sensors and crunch data on the fly, thanks to always-on connectivity. The Internet has connected countless people, devices, sensors, and sectors of business in ways that were unimaginable a few decades ago. The Internet of Everything is changing our work, home, and personal life as more and more devices talk to each other and manage our routines.

A Digital Twin

The physical world that we live in has a limited economy. There is a limited amount of space for buildings, houses, and hours in a day. But once we have a digital copy of the world with a digital economy, it will be nearly unlimited. At the very least, it will be ever-amplifying without the limitations of the physical world. This is where the concept of a digital twin comes in. It's a one-to-one copy of anything in the world. A person could create a virtual replica of themselves, but there could also be a copy of a physical space for meetings, social interaction, the arts, or design. Digital twins integrate IoT, AI, machine learning, and software analytics to create living digital simulation models that update and change as their physical counterparts change.

For example, Tesla "has a digital twin for every car it builds, tied to the car's vehicle identification number (VIN). Data is constantly transmitted back and forth from the car to the factory. For instance, if a driver notices a rattle in a door, it could be fixed by downloading software that tweaks the hydraulics of that particular door. Tesla regularly pushes out software updates to customers' cars based on the data received from them."[20] Employees will need to expand their capacities for work as they manage their physical and digital lives in even more complicated ways.

The Tyranny of the Flat Screen

While the disruptions above are exciting, there is one drawback. If we continue using future technologies the way we do now, many of us will experience serious health problems from our sedentary work and lifestyle.

Meet Emma. She's your co-worker of the future. Her skin is pale and she has dry, red eyes from staring at a computer screen all day. Her wrists and ankles are swollen from repetitive movement, among other ailments. Worst of all, she has a permanently bent back from hours sitting at a computer.

Actually, Emma is a creepy, life-size doll designed by a team of health experts based on survey data submitted by more than 3,000 workers in Europe.[21] As she's displayed in various offices, Emma's terrifying appearance is a warning to people. *This* is what we may look like in twenty years if our workplace environment and habits don't change. The report, entitled "The Work Colleague of the Future," predicts what you or your co-worker will look like in the future due to our incessant hunching over while looking at our smartphones and because of workspaces that are not designed for physical movement.[22]

"The percentages of UK office workers who said they already suffered from sore eyes (50 percent), sore backs (48 percent), and headaches (48 percent) as a direct result of their work environment informed the design of the sickly Emma, who also suffers from stress-related eczema, excess weight, varicose veins due to diminished blood flow, and swollen limbs."[23]

A behavioral futurist who led the study, William Higham, concluded, "Unless we make radical changes to our working lives, such as moving more, addressing our posture at our desks, taking regular walking breaks, or considering improving our workstation setup, our offices are going to make us very sick."[24] He argues that we sit too much (as much as eight years of our lives) and that the hunched back is not only due to looking at our phones but slouching in our chairs at our desks. Different types of desks, more walk and talk meetings, and other changes could prevent us from looking like Emma.[25] There's another solution: Spatial Computing.

Heads Up and Hands-Free

Spatial Computing is a new form of computing that combines artificial intelligence and computer vision to blend that digital content into your reality seamlessly. It comprises several technologies that help people use computers outside of screens and layer them into the real world. It helps us understand the physical world. It's being used to track viruses, steer driverless cars, map oceans, chart endangered species, and create election maps.[26]

Spatial Computing, using an augmented reality headset, enables workers to keep their heads up and their bodies in motion. It's the principle of coming back to the campfire. Before radio and television, when people told stories, they would sit around a campfire and look each other in the eye.

Today, we're looking down at our phones, hunched over, as Emma warned us about. But, we'll soon be able to have a "heads-up" experience and look people in the eye once again as we utilize spatial computing devices. Meron Gribetz once gave a TED Talk that demonstrated his. He showed two people wearing AR headsets, both working around the same hologram, and yet able to still make eye contact with each other. Gribertz explained, "Our mirror-neuron subsystem suggests that we can connect with each other and with our work much better if we can see each other's faces and hands in 3D."[27]

And if you don't like hefty, cumbersome VR headsets, these devices are getting smaller all the time. Meanwhile, engineer and entrepreneurs Peter Diamandis and Steven Kotler say this won't be a problem for long. "[R]esearchers are now using nanotech to create smart contact lenses with a resolution six times greater than today's smartphones."[28]

The convergence of technologies such as AI, voice recognition, 5G, AR, and Spatial Computing, transfers information into glasses or headsets so that we're able to look up, make eye contact, stand up and move while completing complicated tasks as nature intended rather than slouching further down.

Utopia or Dystopia?

Humans are wired to dislike and oppose change, and tend to have a fatalist view of the future. But as futurists, we enjoy thinking about the future, imagining its potential, and offering strategic foresight. In short, we're creatively optimistic! When people think carefully about how complicated people, technology, and the world are, they realize that we don't need to have a dystopian or utopian view. The truth lies somewhere in the middle.

From a logical standpoint, it's more likely that the future will be "protopian." The world won't be perfect and happy, but it won't be an abysmal dystopia either. This means there will be positives and negatives, but overall, it will be a better world. Digital marketing consultant Marcus Wong writes, "Protopia defines a state where we're no longer fighting for survival

(Dystopia), nor are we accepting perfection (Utopia....
Every opportunity to create something new, something
faster, something 'better'—creates a new world of problems
that we would have never initially created. This is not a bad
thing; some problems are good to have."[29] In short, we can't
eliminate problems without introducing new ones. This is
why we will see progress, but not perfection.[30] Will robots
take some workers' jobs? Yes. There will be automation,
but automation will also generate new jobs.

So, if companies understand that the future of the
augmented workforce is neither dystopian or utopian, then
the way they prepare for the future of work changes. They
aren't necessarily always thinking of the worst-case
scenario, nor the perfection of everyone being happy, but a
kind of middle ground.

The Future Belongs to Those
Who Prepare for It Today

Our global workforce is slowly becoming augmented. In
the coming years, most people reading this book who
weren't already part of the augmented workforce will join
it. Surely, your children and grandchildren will be fully a
part of it. We must prepare our workers by giving them
training and access to new technologies. Employees will
need to prepare themselves for the technology shifts that
will transform the workplace forever.

Adapting to big changes and maintaining agility is not
something that most companies and employees train for.
But, if people are trained to unlearn, relearn, and reskill,
they will succeed in the future. We have work to do—
employees, managers, executives and beyond. Many young
men and women are currently studying in a system that
doesn't prepare them for the 21st-century workforce. Our
educational systems are stuck in the industrial age. It
doesn't teach critical thinking, how to develop new skills,
resiliency, and how to unlearn, relearn, and reskill oneself.
It prepares people for one career with the assumption that

tomorrow will look like yesterday. Students aren't taught to imagine what could be, but how to work in what has been.

The notion that a former generation had of working for the same company for decades has been obsolete for two generations at least. We are going to have multiple careers throughout our lives because of a longer lifespan and because of a rapidly changing marketplace. Colleges and universities need to educate themselves about the technological changes that are coming so they can prepare students for a future that will be much different than many presume it will be.

When those students enter the workforce, they'll quickly be left behind if they lack foresight and imagination. As John Sculley, the former CEO of Apple, said, "The future belongs to those who see possibilities before they become obvious."[31]

Companies can help their workforce prepare for the future by starting early. Talk about new technology on the horizon and how that tech will influence which roles and why. Use change management principles to help employees adjust to see AI, for example, as a benefit and not a threat. AI takes over jobs that people tend to find boring. When it's crunch time at the end of the month, you could now go home at five instead of staying late for a month-end close, because the AI would take over these steps. Connecting everything with AI isn't about replacing humans. It's about finding the right balance of human workers and technology. Empower your workforce so that they feel part of the change and not a victim of it.

Here are some tips for the augmented workforce:

- Define your core work. What is it that you enjoy doing most? What is your expertise? Think about how you can do more of what you're good at and what can be taken off your plate with IoT and AI.

- Use incoming tech as an opportunity to upskill. When Amazon brings on temporary workers during the holiday season, they have been able to reduce training time from six weeks to two days with the help of connected robots and augmented training screens.[32]

- How can connected devices and emerging technology help you live your ideal lifestyle? For instance, workers can use it as an opportunity to be a digital nomad, to be home more for their kids, or to be more environmentally friendly and save hours in the day.

In this book, we'll arm you with the knowledge you'll need to seize your own future, augmenting your workforce toward success with AR, AI, and 5G. We'll discuss what the technologies are, how we arrived at this point, how they're being used across industries, and what you can do to get started.

CHAPTER TWO

Our Steady March to Digital Existence

If time travel were possible, it would be interesting to see how a person living in 1880 would react after being brought to beginning of 2020. Would they wonder why people were walking around staring at little devices in their hands? Would they be amazed to see Amazon delivering a package less than twenty-four hours after someone placed the order? What would they think about texting, online dating, Zoom meetings, and streaming movies via Netflix?

Would they be overwhelmed once they learned that they could download just about any song they want to listen to (from Classical to Jazz) or learn from one of thirty-million podcast episodes? Would Siri and Alexa make them jump out of their boots? How would we explain the Internet, VR, and AI to them?

Yet today, technology like augmented reality, artificial intelligence, smartphones, and advanced cellular networks like 5G have become second nature to many people. Workers expect their cell phones to receive service anywhere on the globe. Talking to phones and smart devices has become instinctive. Putting on a virtual reality headset to meet up with friends or to go to a work meeting is no big deal. The ease at which people can use these types of technology has been decades in the making. To understand the future made possible by this convergence of tech, we must first ask, how did we get here?

The Hardware, Software, and Networks That Got Us Here

In 1965 Gordon Moore predicted that "the number of components on an integrated circuit would double every year until it reached an astonishing 65,000 by 1975." When his prediction proved correct, "he revised what has become known as Moore's Law to a doubling of transistors on a chip every two years."[33] This law assured manufacturers and programmers that there would be smaller, faster devices every couple of years. They could confidently design for the future because they could count on the technology to be there. Companies could invent and innovate, knowing that future capabilities were nearly endless.

Moore's Law made it possible for people to think beyond personal computers. Smaller, faster chips meant they could build new types of computing devices like smartphones, virtual reality headsets, augmented reality glasses, smart watches, and smart speakers. Even with smaller, more powerful chips, though, the VR equipment of the '60s was nothing like it is today. Ivan Sutherland and Tom Furness were two inventors who "found the secret of VR in the 60's."[34] In 1968, Sutherland built a system "using computer-generated graphics to show users grid-like rooms."[35] He did this on a device dubbed "The Sword of Damocles" because it was made up of "primitive wireframes and heavy hardware" and hung precariously over users.

The Sword of Damocles was the first stepping stone to augmented reality. In fact, because it was partially see-through, "the device is often cited as both the first AR and first VR headset ever built."[36] Also in the 1960s, Tom Furness developed advanced cockpits and virtual interfaces for the U.S. Department of Defense. He is credited as a pioneer in developing virtual reality as well as augmented reality and teaches Industrial and Systems Engineering at the University of Washington.[37] Training pilots virtually increased safety, saved money, and enabled the possibility of introducing dangerous or diverse scenarios with unlimited practice attempts.

Unfortunately for Sutherland and Furness, the hardware and software weren't at a point for mass adoption. It wouldn't be until the 1990s that virtual reality would get its next comeback. VR would continue to grow in the enterprise but, until then, it was largely forgotten by the public.

The World Wide Web

Of course, none of this would have been the same without the accelerant that was the World Wide Web. "In the eighties and early nineties, the conventional wisdom was that the real action online was inside the great walled garden of AOL, CompuServe, and Prodigy."[38] In 1994, Jim Clark and Marc Andreessen founded Netscape which "laid the foundation for virtually every technology that defines today's online experience."[39] It opened up the door for countless websites and technologies not dependent on the AOL ecosystem.

During the 1990s, almost anyone who started an Internet company could get funding. "Surfing the web" was coined, the browser war took place, and major companies that we know today, such as Amazon, Craigslist, and eBay, went live. Netflix was founded during the dot-com era and so was Google.[40] Necessarily, the Internet bubble burst in 2000, but the '90s showed that connectivity was the future.

VR in the '90s

In the 1990s, virtual reality got a revival as the company Virtuality, Inc. became its best-known creator. Their bulky headsets and accompanying machines, which were used for entertainment and even found at restaurants such as Dave & Buster's, were novel but cumbersome. Decades later, Oculus founder, Palmer Luckey, considered purchasing a Virtuality device to build his headset but was dissuaded from doing so. In 1984, Tom Zimmerman invented the DataGlove.[41] The DataGlove had continuous sensors which made it possible for creatives to think beyond the click and drag capabilities of the mouse. It opened up the world of gestures that we use today.

In the 1980s, Zimmerman joined Jaron Lanier to start Visual Programming Language (VPL). VPL was "programming inside a video game, rather than about a video game in some external text language."[42] This was, in a way, the beginning of the modern-day "game engine" concept. Kids could watch the coding action attached to each picture, then collect them into an order that would make a subroutine.[43] The DataGlove was the input device for VPL, making it the first gesture-based programming language.

Even though virtual reality was brimming with life in Silicon Valley, most people believed VR was merely something from science fiction. Then, in 1992, Brett Leonard released a movie called *Lawnmower Man* (adapted from a Stephen King story). It was "one of the first depictions in mass culture of the immersive three-dimensional medium known as virtual reality" and is a cult classic today.[44] Tom Zimmerman recalls seeing the DataGlove used by Pierce Brosnan in the film: "'You're going to break the fiber optics. You're tugging it too hard.' It was really amazing to see my brainchild come to life."[45] *Lawnmower Man* helped people to see the enormous potential of VR.

In 1989, Nintendo released the Power Glove, designed for the Nintendo Entertainment System (NES). The Power Glove sold for $100 and worked by plugging directly into the game console. It could pick up finger and hand movements and track accuracy to within a quarter of an inch. It was the first video game controller that allowed players to operate Nintendo games with intuitive hand gestures.[46] Kids loved playing boxing or driving games, feeling in control with their body and immersed in the game.

There is still a bit of a cult following of the Power Glove today. People have even hacked the glove in order to create music with it. Unfortunately, the glove was not well-made and offered subpar gameplay, so it only sold about 100,000 units.[47] And since it was wired into the main unit, mobility was limited. Still, the "Power Glove's top-notch marketing transfixed a generation of young gamers."[48] The Power Glove had success in pop culture, inspiring Nintendo and other game manufacturing companies to continue making devices for gesture-based gaming.

Augmented and Virtual Reality in the 2010s

Augmented reality places virtual overlays and objects in the user's physical reality. We access it through phones, tablets, and some head-mounted displays. In April of 2012, Google released its first augmented reality glasses: Google Glass.[49] It was a device in the right place, at the wrong time. Google Glass failed to define what it was good for—everyday day use, work, games, or one-off situations. Its battery life paled in comparison to smartphones. Mostly, people weren't ready for a camera watching everything they did as privacy concerns were not adequately addressed.[50] People feared being secretly recorded on video by a Glass wearer. Some businesses and restaurants banned its use on their premises. A term was even coined to describe some people who wore the device in socially-unacceptable ways: "glasshole."[51]

In 2015, Google ended the Glass Explorer program. While not officially shelved, Glass disappeared from the consumer market.[52] However, Google handed the program to Tony Fadell, who's known as "the father of the iPod."[53] Following his contributions, Google Glass is now coming back through robust enterprise uses and may one day reemerge for consumers.

Google wasn't the only company interested in making virtual headsets. Oculus launched their Kickstarter in the summer of 2012. Their Kickstarter video could arguably be the rebirth of virtual reality for developers with endorsements from legendary video game developer John Carmack and Valve's Gabe Newell and Michael Abrash. In the video, Abrash says, "[Oculus Rift] could be the beginning of a whole new industry that leads us eventually to having true augmentation all the time."[54] Oculus's Kickstarter blew past the initial goal of raising $250,000. The campaign raised a whopping $2,437,429 with over 9,500 backers.[55] The world was now eager for VR as Oculus positioned itself as the leader in VR gaming.

While early Oculus products required many wires, sensors, and even an Xbox controller, one of the appeals of its newer model was that it had no wires and no longer needed a computer. Oculus Quest is an all-in-one gaming system that can be played anywhere and utilizes hand-tracking (hands-free) and gestures (with controllers). Now, their technology is being used in other fields, from healthcare to automotive industries.

In March 2014, Mark Zuckerberg, CEO of Facebook, bought Oculus for $2.3 billion.[56] The acquisition surprised the Oculus team itself. Zuckerberg told them, "I think this has the potential…to not just be the next gaming platform, but the next real computing platform."[57]

Augmented Reality's First Breakout Hit

Global game sensation Pokémon was already a well-loved franchise, but in 2016 they put themselves back on the map with *Pokémon Go*. For the first time, people could "catch" Pokémon in real life via the augmented reality app, *Pokémon Go*. The game quickly turned into a worldwide phenomenon, grossing $100 million in its first twenty days. At its peak, the game had forty-five million active users worldwide and over 500 million downloads.[58]

The game launched with around 150 species of Pokémon but increased to about six-hundred by 2020. Pokémon Go also inspired many marketing campaigns, showing businesses that augmented reality apps were more than fun and games.[59] Many local businesses advertised in the game which dramatically increased foot traffic and sales.

Networks

Cellular networks have their own unique history. They have come a long way since people toted around brick-sized cell phones in the early 1970s. The first generation of mobile networks, 1G, rolled out across the world after it was first launched in Tokyo in 1979. The coverage was poor and there was no roaming support or compatibility between systems. Calls weren't encrypted which meant anyone with a radio scanner could drop in on a call. That didn't stop Motorola's DynaTac from racking up "20 million global subscribers by 1990."[60]

Cellular networks rapidly influenced culture and how people communicated with each other. 2G made it possible to text and send photos and multimedia messages. 3G standardized network protocols used by vendors. During the 3G era, video streaming became possible. People became comfortable with watching anything from news, sports, and entertainment in the palm of their hand. Voice over IP companies such as Skype launched and the first iPhone was released in the last couple of years of 3G networks. These technologies impacted everything from international meetings without flights and working from home to long-distance relationships.

4G is what most people use today. It made high-quality video streaming and mobile web access possible. 4G required device manufacturers to design products specifically for 4G, which has led to Apple becoming the world's first trillion-dollar company.[61]

Putting Technology to Work

Xerox's Palo Alto Research Center changed the office forever. It was the first computer designed from the ground up to support an operating system based on a graphical user interface (GUI). And, it eventually developed the desktop metaphor.[62] Bob Taylor, who ran PARC's Computer Science Lab believed that "the [Alto] machines would be transformational, eliminating much of what he called the 'drudgery of office work' and freeing office workers 'to attend to higher-level functions so necessary to a human's estimate of his own worth.'"[63] This is the same argument that many today make for artificial intelligence and its siblings, machine learning and robotic process automation.

Arguments against AI in the workplace say that not everyone is capable of doing higher-level jobs. And if they are, there might not be enough available. According to a 1987 report from the Bureau of Labor Statistics, "concern about changing technology has been continual over our history."[64] The report found that relatively few people were laid off because of technological change (computers, robots, flexible manufacturing systems, and other office productivity technology). In fact, clerical workers (the group most expected to face unemployment due to computers) increased, "offset[ting] jobs eliminated by the computer."

Plus, "the introduction of computers made possible work that was previously impractical because it would have been too costly and time-consuming."[65] The introduction of the computer in the office resulted in new job opportunities. New industries related to computer manufacturing emerged as well.

T.L. Andrews has shown that "despite the fact that 98-percent of the functions of making materials have now been automated, the number of weaving jobs has increased since the nineteenth century."[66] Peter Diamandis and Steven Kotler state, "The same thing is true for paralegals and law clerks, two professions predicted to suffer job loss as a result of AI. Yet discovery software, introduced into law firms in the 1990s, has actually led to the inverse. Turns out, AI is so good at discovery that lawyers now need more humans to sift through the deluge—so paralegal employment has increased."[67] In a similar way, ATMs increased efficiency and lowered costs, which led to more banks being built, which led to more human employment.

A study of 1,500 companies by *Harvard Business Review* revealed that companies "achieve the most significant performance improvements when humans and machines work together."[68] This same article warned against displacing employees and instead, encouraged leaders to look for ways for humans to partner with machines and AI. For instance, BMW saw an 85-percent increase in productivity when they replaced their traditional (i.e., automated) assembly line process with human/robot teams.[69]

We are likely to see similar growth regarding jobs and efficiency with AI, AR, and 5G. The VR industry is growing, "with the market size of consumer virtual reality hardware and software projected to increase from 6.2 billion U.S. dollars in 2019 to more than 16 billion U.S. dollars by 2022."[70] Augmented reality is forecasted to reach over 95 million users in the U.S. by 2022.[71] These numbers mean companies are investing in spatial computing technology, either as a core product or as a way to complement their value chain.

Demographic Changes

Technology has changed our culture and the ways people communicate. It has also changed the way generations relate to one another. The millennial generation was the last to grow up without the Internet immediately being available to them. The Internet came of age as many millennials did. It shaped their outlook on work and society, leaving their baby boomer parents in the dust. Just as their parents thought they finally caught up to social media by taking over Facebook, millennials and Gen Z (the Internet generation) fled to other platforms.

For Generation Z, the Internet and smart devices are part of, or an extension of, their identity.[72] They grew up with the Internet, and a vast majority of them don't remember a time without a smartphone or tablet in front of their face. For Gen Z, technology is less intentional and more intuitive. To be friends is to interact through a web of apps (Instagram, WhatsApp, Facetime, TikTok). "Tech is seamlessly and vitally integrated into their friendships." Their "social skills are morphing into a hybrid of technology and face-to-face contact."[73]

This way of using technology for social life is telling for how Gen Z and future generations expect to interact with the world. Going to class or work in virtual reality, interacting with humanoid robots, or having an AI best friend won't seem out of place. It will be the continued extension of the lives they already expect.

Behavioral Changes

There is no doubt that cell phones and artificial intelligence change the way people behave. Memes show groups of people on their phones instead of talking with each other. In the past two decades, technology has become so reliable that people no longer memorize their important phone numbers. People ask their phones for advice or directions instead of others. Friendship is measured in the number of "likes" on social media.

"Text Neck" was a term invented to describe the pain people feel from looking at their smartphones in the wrong way.[74] Hunched over, slouching, and neck bent, the damage can be irreversible. Dr. Bolash stated, "Research shows that for every inch you drop your head forward, you double the load on those muscles. Looking down at your smartphone, with your chin to your chest, can put about 60 pounds of force on your neck.... Sitting in a slumped position restricts your lungs' ability to expand, impairing your lung capacity. Inhaling less oxygen means your heart needs to pump harder to distribute more oxygen-carrying blood through your body."[75]

Parents worry about children's screen time but are often oblivious to their own device usage. Studies have shown that teens spend anywhere from six to ten hours a day on their smartphones. But, adults spend at least three hours a day on their phones, with about 2,600 taps, swipes, or touches a day (and an average of almost one-hundred phone pickups a day, nearly every ten minutes, which has increased substantially over just the last few years[76]). We could consider that middle schools teach proper smartphone habits as part of their health classes. Cell phones tend to make parents less emotionally present, termed "distracted parenting."[77] Considering how much time teens and adults spend on these devices, learning from Dr. Bolash's advice could increase everyone's health.

The dopamine hit that comes from checking email, getting likes on social media, or receiving text messages, has become addictive for many.[78] "Platforms like Facebook, Snapchat, and Instagram leverage the very same neural circuitry used by slot machines and cocaine to keep us using their products as much as possible…Every notification, whether it's a text message, a 'like' on Instagram, or a Facebook notification, has the potential to be a positive social stimulus and dopamine influx."[79]

Apps for workers take advantage of these addictive behaviors as well. Work is gamified as programs, like Slack, bring employees back to the app, preventing them from focusing on deep work. Work email follows employees home, creating an "always on" mentality. As the pandemic forces more people to adapt to working remotely, home becomes the office. Video calls bring employee's personal lives to work as the camera is a window into their home and family life.

As technology advances, it may become less addictive as we engage in more natural user interfaces. "Digital minimalism" has gained movement over the years as a method for people to detach from their devices.[80] Products like LightPhone 2 were specifically designed to wean people off their smartphone addiction and to help them be more present in their daily lives.[81] Thanks to smartphones, humans now have a shorter attention span than a goldfish.[82] "Microsoft found that since the year 2000 (or about when the mobile revolution began), the average attention span dropped from twelve seconds to eight seconds."[83]

Not all behavioral changes from technology are bad. Technology enables people to think in more creative ways, like becoming a YouTube content creator or starting a Facebook business. People feel connected, even physically present when playing an Internet-enabled game or in virtual reality. Wearables like FitBit and step trackers that are built into smartphones motivate people to work out more consistently. As people move to where jobs are, friendships become long distance. But with technology like social media, web meetings, social fitness apps, and spatial computing that allow for immersive experiences, friends and family don't have to feel as isolated as they may have just two decades ago.

Millennials and Gen Z have spurred technological change by the way they use it. Millennials influenced how we watch TV by "cutting the cord," making streaming services like Netflix more powerful than cable. MaryLeigh Bliss, chief content officer at Ypulse, said Gen Z is "pivoting entertainment to be a more mobile-focused enterprise that's shifting the industry as well as advertising."[84] Similar positive disruptions will occur as 5G, AI, and VR become more mainstream.

What This Means

Technology has changed the way people work, play, communicate, and experience the world. Adoption of the latest devices and mobile technology will continue, but how people use it could change as interfaces to devices become more vocal (voice technology and AI) and less screen-oriented. Cell phones were the first generation of tech that was widely adopted that let consumers see the world in a new way. Wearables like smart glasses, neuro-tech headphones that can read one's mind, and smartwatches that can sense brain patterns will continue to change how people operate at work and in their daily lives.

The traditional idea of "manual labor" will come into question as robots start taking center stage outside of manufacturing. At the same time, augmented and virtual reality will allow for even broader groups of people to come to work, such as those with mental disabilities because they will be brain-assisted. New technology creates new opportunities, and if you can focus on that rather than fearing change, your future will be ripe for the digital picking.

Where We're Going

Despite the differences between generations, the technological gap is closing. While the millennial generation uses social media the most, followed closely by Gen X, baby boomers and the Silent Generation are quickly catching up. Since 2012, the use of Facebook has grown the fastest amongst older generations.[85] While baby boomers trail younger generations in smartphone adoption, their rates in adoption are growing. In 2011, only 25 percent of baby boomers reported owning a cell phone. In 2019, 68 percent did. As older generations stay in the workforce longer, adoption of smartphones and other technology is enhancing their ability to keep working.

For the past few years, technologists have predicted that Moore's Law is coming to an end. It came to a point where making a smaller chip or transistor would cause the chip to be unstable. That doesn't mean the end of technology and innovation. It means exponential growth will take place in other areas of technology.

The past has taught us that many ideas about augmented and virtual reality, artificial intelligence, and cellular networks are not new. Their potential has been known for years. But it takes time to perfect, understand, and properly utilize various technologies. By studying and learning from previous generations, technology can continue to improve humanity for the better.

CHAPTER THREE

Your New Global Computer: Building the Future on Six Pillars

In this chapter we break down these tech buzzwords: Internet of Things (IoT), artificial intelligence (AI), the cloud, blockchain, extended reality (XR), and 5G. We hope to reframe your world through these six technological pillars of the computing landscape so that your profession or business can benefit. Clear understanding of the six pillars and how they are reshaping the future will help you explain them to your workforce.

However, it takes more than mere familiarity to adopt these technologies in a way that will positively transform your organization. Unfortunately, this is where a number of business leaders allow their excitement to get the better of them. The new computing landscape commands significant costs and requires well-thought-out designs and strategies to ensure a successful roll-out. Experimenting without the right insight can hinder your growth plans and perhaps even damage your business's brand.

We're definitely not saying companies shouldn't toy around with these technologies. After all, experimentation is an essential part of learning. Instead, we recommend having a clear strategy before you deploy these tools. Based on their track record, these technologies can spawn unintended—and often embarrassing—consequences. Just recall the backlash incurred by Microsoft and Twitter when they launched a flawed AI that could easily be corrupted by users.[86] Startups with dreams of scaling-up can learn valuable lessons from these kinds of tech giant blunders—sure, be bold and brazen, but balance your big ambitions with modesty and caution.

To be fair, it doesn't take much to misconstrue the potential benefits of these technologies. After all, vendors offering products that include AI, IoT, AR, and similar technologies have been known to make impressive promises only to break them, disappointingly, in the end. And here's the rub: the less business leaders know about these technologies, the more likely they'd believe in and bankroll very expensive failures.

The key is to be open, and not feel intimidated. To stop worrying and to start imagining how these technologies influence the nature of work, enhance individual performance, and lift organizational efficiency. To decide which mix of XR, AI, connected devices, and the blockchain make the biggest ROI or upgrade employees the most, focus on the problem you're trying to solve.

We have identified six technologies that are having a deep and far-ranging impact on how we live our lives and do business today and the near term. These specific technologies may seem fragmented, each occupying a separate corner in the scheme of things. But they are not.

In fairness, it is easy to see these technologies individually and ask, "So where should I place my bet?" But that's the wrong way to look at the picture. A much better way is to view all these technologies as multiple instruments playing together in a symphony orchestra and ask, "Which one resonates with me the most? Which will help my business win?"

Getting closer to home, these technologies may also be viewed as interdependent components of the ultimate, next-gen computer. To make it easier to visualize their main focus and relevance, in the following list and subsequent sections, we used familiar analogies to describe each technology. You can—for example—think of artificial intelligence as apps and the cloud as a hard drive. Hopefully, doing this blunts the hard edges of technical learning and demystifies these amazing technologies.

1. **Input**: Something that allows you to input data such as a mouse or a keyboard **(IoT)**

2. **Apps:** A software program designed for a specific purpose such as a mobile app **(Artificial Intelligence)**

3. **Storage:** Somewhere to store and manage information such as a hard disk or USB flash drives **(Cloud Storage)**

4. **Security:** A system for accessing, protecting, and securing your personal data such as passwords and other authentication mechanisms **(Blockchain)**

5. **Display:** A screen where you can interact with information such as an LED monitor **(Extended Reality)**

6. **Network**: A device that enables your computer to hook up with the Internet such as a modem **(5G)**

The Internet of Things:
Many Inputs

For years, we've heard about the Internet of Things (IoT), with its billions of devices enabling smart-everything connections everywhere. The Internet of Things describes a network of physical objects that are embedded with sensors, software, and other technology like bluetooth or wireless capabilities to talk to each other over the Internet. IoT is all about input. Just as keyboards wait for commands, and mice and touchpads wait for clicks, IoT distributes the next-generation "computer" knowledge of what's going on across a range of devices. In the context of this book, IoT is an ingredient, so it's not getting a lot of mention. Much in the way people don't talk much about mice and keyboards when it comes to computers. The concept of a computer is growing larger than one device. Between the cloud, 5G, XR, and AI, a computer is becoming a networked intelligence with tendrils extending to many corners of our physical reality.

The Internet of Things takes place in your home. Think, a security system that's connected to your thermostat. The thermostat goes on standby when the house is set to "away" and it kicks back on when the alarm is turned off. IoT connects a myriad of sensors that measure and track everything: water use, equipment health, traffic, air quality, biometrics, construction tools, and many others. IoT works with mountains and mountains of data to make the world more efficient and safer.

Over the years, industry insiders have been predicting that the billions of devices we use will start talking with each other to extend our capabilities and make our lives more convenient. This is already happening—but at different paces across different industries and in different locations around the globe. These connected devices include a wide array of instrumentation, gadgets, and appliances used for the most mundane needs such as toasters all the way up to air traffic control radars. These things exchange information in real time to make sure that our lives go seamlessly from one activity to the next.

On the technical side, think of IoT as a system of computer chips and network radios inside a lot of different devices located around the planet. From keyboards to cameras, IoT uses such devices to see and interact with the real world. And by capturing and analyzing heaps of real-world data, IoT offers people and organizations smarter choices on how to do things more efficiently. IoT encompasses every sphere of human activity:

Where You Live

IoT has already made significant headway into the smart home segment, where the things you commonly use are interconnected into a domestic grid. It could be your thermostat, toothbrush, and refrigerator. It's your Alexa-powered microwave and lighting. It's your security cameras, doorbell, door locks, and alarm systems working in tandem.

Where You Work

On the organizational and professional side, IoT is widely used in shipping and logistics. Some companies use IoT to track their assets such as field equipment and power tools located on a jobsite. For example, one company uses IoT to determine the location of all their rechargeable cordless drills, how many times each drilled a hole, how deep those holes were, and how often bits were switched. In effect, IoT successfully transformed a jobsite into a connected toolbox. Another company produces IoT-enabled wearables to improve workplace safety for jobs requiring the use of elevated platforms such as scissor lifts. By setting off alarms or shutting systems down when safety harnesses aren't properly attached, the IoT solution effectively saves human lives. Maintenance technicians working on tall communication towers are exposed to much higher risk of death and injury compared to the average employee. IoT-enabled safeguards can dramatically reduce these risks.

In the Community

IoT also offers immense benefits for governments and the public sector. One mundane area where it is making a huge difference is traffic management. As data sharing standards are established, IoT can facilitate real-time communication between vehicles, buildings, and other infrastructure to develop smart road systems that don't require traffic lights. Cars can find and select a parking space before they arrive at their destination. An ambulance may soon be able to reroute traffic in front of it to reach the hospital more efficiently.

Artificial Intelligence: Your Apps

From utopian predictions to dystopian warnings, AI has fascinated humans to the point where some fear its rise (as depicted in stories such as Mary Shelley's *Frankenstein*, and movies such as Stanley Kubrick's *2001: A Space Odyssey* and Alex Garland's *Ex Machina*) while others warm up to its romantic variants (as depicted in Spike Jonze's film *Her*).

Because many experts want AI to approach—and perhaps surpass—the most advanced human thinking, it has been elevated to a place of mythic proportions. As a result, many people tend to accept just about anything you say about it. AI is certainly amazing, but it should not become a hodge-podge of inaccuracies.

To bring artificial intelligence into proper perspective, focus on its practical aspects instead of delving too deeply into the abstract concepts that surround it. One easy way to do that is to treat AI as just another—albeit a supercharged—app.

Throughout the history of technology, we have used tools toward a specific goal. For computers, that means applications or programs that steer computing power. However, with a sea of sensors gathering data, stand-alone apps are no longer equal to the task. Meanwhile, humans neither have time nor the capability to comprehend, measure, and analyze the vast amounts of data accumulating in the "cloud." So we started teaching computers the things we want to do, but don't want to or can't do on our own. Artificial Intelligence is rising to meet that challenge.

Mostly, we let powerful computers that can be directed by AI to perform mind-boggling tasks their own way. Through "deep learning," AI uses human-established rules and expansive sets of data to 1) learn how to interpret information quickly and 2) make smart recommendations or suggest next steps. Reinforced by AI and IoT, computers learn to "see" our world, working as autonomous machines that can "learn" what things mean. AI can organize vast amounts of information, identify patterns, and deliver insight. Because of its enormous computing power, this technology is being used to tackle some of the world's biggest challenges from disease detection and land traffic management to poverty alleviation and climate change.

Many organizations are pushing the horizons of artificial intelligence, aiming to make AI less artificial by hyperfocusing on one field. Natural Language Understanding (NLU) is one excellent example. NLU is used in voice technology products like Alexa, as well as in the company Soul Machines's photorealistic chatbots and virtual humans, who attempt to decode what we say to infer or convey emotions.[87]

Brain–machine interface (BMI) is another example. BMI is a system where information transmitted by the human brain is used to control computer software or a robotic mechanism. BMIs in the form of assisted-living devices make it possible for people with motor or sensory disabilities to carry out daily tasks they could not otherwise perform.

We predict that AI will not only improve humanity's ability to thrive but will also help humans know how to better interact with technology. As technology advances, so does our ability to analyze and adapt to these technologies. This is due, in large part, to the technologies themselves, with AI and computer-driven data helping humans to find new ways to improve their usage. People need not fear change. Instead, as they see the harmony that can be achieved between man and machine, a brighter future is inevitable.

The Cloud: Your New Hard Drive

As technology becomes cheaper and better, more people and businesses gain access to enormous computing power. Computing resources that were once scarce and prohibitively expensive are now so plentiful you can rent them for pennies. But more importantly, you can leverage their remarkable capabilities to handle virtually any task, from modest admin work to world-changing research.

The cloud is one such resource. Cloud computing has many aspects but unlimited data storage is arguably its most compelling feature. After all, "limitless storage" was considered a fantasy among hardcore computer users in the final decades of the 20th century before becoming a dream-come-true in the mid-2000s.

During that thirty-odd year period, we transitioned from silicon memory chips to removable diskettes to high-capacity hard disk drives, and from CD-ROMs to tiny, but high-capacity thumb drives and ultra-fast storage on a chip. Storage used to be super-expensive, so we used it sparingly. And we had to wait a really long time (by today's standards) to read and write data, with the computer all the while chugging along as its limited computing power struggled to process data within a small-storage, low-memory environment. At the time, we were somehow comforted by blinking lights and on-screen progress bars that assured us *something* was happening as we waited.

Today, storage is so plentiful that businesses and individuals can have gigabytes of data space for free. If that isn't enough, both can have terabytes (thousands of gigabytes) of storage at bargain costs. This new reality represents orders of magnitude of more capacity than before. The floppy drive used in the 1980s and '90s generally had a 1.44 MB capacity while most internal hard drives during the same period clocked in at 100 MB to 500 MB, and rarely exceeded 1 gigabyte of storage.

Cloud hosting providers such as Amazon—which has been renting out its servers for the last fifteen years—now enjoy the tailwinds of a cloud-driven economy. Indeed, cloud computing has become an indispensable asset for businesses of all types and sizes today. With videos and high-resolution graphics becoming integral tools across industries, most companies have fully embraced the convenience and capacity of cloud hosting services.

Even online games need to run on top of cloud servers to ensure the best experiences for players. The hugely popular game Fortnite, for example, is now played by over 350 million people. Processing game data for all these players wouldn't be possible without cloud technology. According to an Amazon blog post,[88] Fortnite dealt with two petabytes of data per month in 2018. That means the game—which had 125 million players at the time and generated an estimated revenue of $2.4 billion for game creator Epic Games in the same year— required a stack of at least 2,000 terabyte-hard drives to operate, storage totaling two million gigabytes per month!

What's less obvious in this arrangement is the fact that cloud storage achieves a lot more than just giving companies plenty of space to dump their data. Storing data in the cloud also augments a system's computing power—exponentially.

In essence, the cloud has already solved the perennial problem of data storage. People used to travel to an actual storage site. Now, we have it available all the time "in the ether," and people auto-upload their camera shots to Adobe's, Google's, or Apple's hard drive on the cloud each time they take a picture. We store practically all our personal data—from the mundane to the critical—inside powerful and redundant servers that make up the cloud. Our photos, videos, likes, shares, searches, medical data, taxes, and money all reside in some (hopefully secure) corner online. Indeed, the cloud has finally become the default venue for storing anything that can be represented digitally.

Blockchain: Your New Login and Password

In many instances, specific bits of data swirling around the cloud need to be secured and protected. You want to keep your bank accounts and financial transactions secret, for example. You want contracts, email correspondences, design patents, and sensitive business dealings strictly confidential. On social networks, you may want to share personal information only to people you trust such as friends and family, preventing other entities and the general public from gawking at awkward chapters of your life.

Given the increasing risks, gravity, and cases of data theft and other cybercrimes, conventional safeguards such as logins and passwords certainly need an upgrade. Based on an overwhelming consensus among cybersecurity experts, blockchain technology might be the ultimate security upgrade the digital economy needs. And it all started with an innovative idea of linking different blocks of data securely.

Bitcoin is a virtual medium of exchange that disrupted markets, thrilled everyday investors, and goosed bankers during the early years of its emergence. Having pioneered the field, Bitcoin has become synonymous with the more generic, yet still somewhat obscure term "cryptocurrency."

Bitcoin excites cybersecurity experts because of the technological concept upon which it operates. This concept is often referred to as Distributed Ledger Technology (DLT), a permanent, unchangeable record of any transaction, including transfers of ownership, payments, handshakes, signatures, and a lot more—aka, blockchain.

Blockchain is a type of digitally encrypted or secure "signature" that complements the cadre of exponential technologies we have so far identified. That is, not only will we hold and store stuff that matters to us in the cloud, we would also need to keep it permanently

secured. If you own something, no one can take it away from you. But if you give it away, you can never get it back.

Originally developed as a decentralized approach to managing cryptocurrency, blockchain technology offers enormous potential in radically improving many other fields: asset/ownership security, data protection, central banking and financial institutions, fraud prevention, and business relationship automation via "smart contracts." In fact, given its broad utility,[89] blockchain is already being used in healthcare, food safety, environmental protection, humanitarian efforts, fashion, and the jewelry market.

Meanwhile, English singer-songwriter and Grammy awardee Imogen Heap reportedly uses blockchain to ensure all her songs correctly credit everyone who participated in their creation and release.[90] Heap's aim is to build a "fair trade" music industry that bypasses music labels and music streaming services to give musicians and their teams of producers, writers, and engineers more ownership over the data and money generated by their work.

Blockchain helps ensure that the right things happen at the right time, automatically, and with zero chance for shenanigans. Pretty soon, we might even find its application in the voting booth, both to prevent real election fraud as well as to silence sore losers.

Extended Reality (XR): Your New Display

In her book, *Augmented Human: How Technology Is Shaping the New Reality*, Helen Papagiannis writes about breaking through the glass.[91] That's what extended reality is. It's an interface that incorporates all of our senses: touch, sight, hearing, smell, and taste. The industry is still nailing down the terms, but essentially extended reality (XR) and spatial computing are the same. It's a blend of augmented and virtual reality that goes beyond the screen, providing a more natural way of interacting with the digital world. To fully understand extended reality, let's break down the different technologies that it's made of.

Augmented Reality

Augmented reality (AR) overlays the digital on top of physical reality. When you see someone use a face filter to give themselves bunny ears, that's AR. AR is also the vibrations from your smartwatch reminding you to move. There are even digital smell and taste devices but they are lesser used forms of AR. Augmented reality is built into our phones and in smart glasses like Snapchat's Spectacles.

Let's walk through an airport with AR. Your AR glasses show a GPS-enabled virtual line on the ground telling you the distance to your gate. You ask the AI built into the AR glasses where the airline's lounge is. The glasses reroute you. They also overlay a digital menu of what's available at the lounge. You click your food choices so that they'll be ready when you arrive. Your smartwatch buzzes three times, alerting you that your flight is boarding. As you walk past the gate digitally recreates smells of Cinnabon, drawing you to what is actually a vending machine. No fresh Cinnabons available.

Virtual Reality

Virtual reality is stepping into a completely virtual world. Other equipment like haptic gloves and omni-directional VR treadmills further immerse you into the virtual world. Virtual reality is a powerful tool that is shown to affect empathy, increases retention, and improves engagement.

Immerse is one company that uses VR to transform the employee experience. In one case study, Immerse used their platform to simulate an accidental overspill on a storage tanker.[92] This scenario is difficult and dangerous to train in real life, but VR can recreate these scenarios in a safe, repeatable and cost-effective way. Trainees can take the same simulation multiple times to see how they improve. And the company can monitor each trainee's progress with data from the simulation.

Virtual reality on the cloud makes scaling content possible. Set up for advanced training takes less time and companies can put more people through the simulation at a time. Virtual reality has many other uses from pain management for patients in hospitals to prototyping and virtual meetings (goodbye 2D video calls).

Volumetric Video

Volumetric video captures real life people and objects in 3D—also known as holograms. Remember when R2D2 showed a hologram of Princess Leia in *Star Wars: A New Hope*? That is volumetric video. Avatar Dimension is a volumetric capture studio in Washington D.C. They use 70 of IOI's 12 megapixel Volucam cameras to create holograms.[93] Avatar Dimension helps clients capture volumetric video for cases like training and entertainment. People can interact with holograms in VR or AR. Extended reality is the ultimate user interface. It will open up our world to information, entertainment, and experiences that aren't available to us with smartphones. Extended reality will continue to encompass other emerging technologies. This unified and frameless display will bring all available data into context. Tied to place with GPS and other mapping and sensing technologies, the "AR Cloud" will encapsulate how computers, sensors, and robots see the world and how they interact with us.

5G: Your New Network

Before the World Wide Web debuted in 1989, people needed a hardline connection to the Internet (whose origins date back in the 1960s). There were no browsers per se. Local Area Networks (LANs) connected computers to each other and other LANs through a few specific applications like Telnet, FTP, or Archie, but you couldn't do much other than upload, download, and chat.

From this "data phase" of Internet technology, we eventually transitioned to the "content and context phase," where the Web connected vast amounts of published information on websites as well as active social networks such as Facebook, LinkedIn, and Twitter. The next phase is one where the AR Cloud seamlessly connects people, places, and things.

The journey to get from one phase to the final one is hardly a smooth ride. Especially when it comes to the telecommunication standards (1G to 5G) through which data flows. Here are some of the milestones of that eventful journey:

- **Dial-up Internet access**: used a noisy modem to link the public switched telephone network with Internet service providers; flaky connection; metered pay-as-you-go; you had to hang up the voice call so that you could allow Internet data to flow

- **1G**: first generation wireless technology; used analog communications standards

- **2G**: second generation wireless cellular technology; initial shift from analog to digital standards; made incremental improvements in network speed and data capacity

- **Early broadband**: used either ISDN and T1 lines; was expensive and rare at the time

- **Hi-speed Internet**: excited homes and made offices more productive

- **Wi-fi technology**: emerged by the turn of the century; set us free from the cable; extended the capabilities of smartphones, tablets, printers, cameras, vehicles, wearables, and drones.

- **3G**: facilitated the growth of the mobile web and the rise of apps

- **4G**: faster than 3G but still second class

- **5G**: considered by technologists and industry observers as the true mobile broadband; delivers wi-fi-type experience away from home

Experts predict that the set of standards and technologies comprising 5G will eventually connect IoT inputs, cloud storage, AI applications, and AR products to build and maintain the metaverse. When this event happens, your computer will no longer just sit on your desk, backpack, or pocket. It will be everywhere. Computing will be like the air all around you—tracking everything, crunching data, and always ready to serve. You won't even need to ponder how long it will take to download a 50 GB game or a full movie in 4K resolution.

It is easy to fixate over this upgrade, take a short view of things, and miss the bigger picture. We just might be so taken in by the newfound convenience that we fail to notice the quantum leap happening before our eyes.

In some places, actual 5G is already available, and it's more than just a marketing ploy. In those places, no one is waiting on the delivery of data anymore. All the data you need is ever present, and you can access it almost instantaneously. Amid all the buzz that surrounds it, 5G achieves something many have thought impossible, effectively taking us to an extraordinary milestone: the end of waiting.

All Things Fall into Place

Whatever you think of these technologies, they're more powerful taken together than alone. AI, blockchain, IoT, XR, cloud, and 5G represent the key components of the uber-computer. They are your inputs, your apps, your storage, and your screen. They are meant to solve global challenges, transform the way we work, and dramatically change our world for the better.

The future is already here and the pieces are converging. Our collective hunger for efficiency, convenience, and great experiences are driving seemingly fragmented technologies to sync, fuse, and supercharge the way we benefit from data. The worker of today is becoming transformed into a super-being. One with access to information from the machines and products they work with every day. Converging technology will help workers interact with each other, enforcing stronger teams and collaboration. As business leaders incorporate these technologies as one solution, they'll better understand their employees and customers.

In every industry and business niche around the world, the six technology pillars outlined in this chapter are finding a broad and surprising range of applications. From recruitment and training to product design and marketing, these technologies impact virtually every department of an organization and every aspect of running a business.

Part II:
Gradually, Then
Suddenly—Exponential
Change Is Upon Us

CHAPTER FOUR

The Future Is Already Here: Augmented Workforces

We've examined the six pillars of emerging technology and traced the path to show how we got to now. Now it's time to learn what's happening in fast-evolving industries. Take a whirlwind tour of your own with these quick hits by industry leaders to spark your imagination and build confidence that you can augment *your* workforce! Feel free to jump around the next few chapters or read them all. You may even find ideas for your colleagues in other industries as well. Later, we'll learn how to apply your newfound inspiration.

What Will an Augmented Workforce Look Like?

IoT, AI, blockchain, XR, and 5G will radically transform nearly every industry and facet of life. They will fundamentally change how people are educated and trained, as well as how they do their work. These technologies will bring about a new way of living, which those from the past may not recognize, but those who grow up with them will never question. They will be a seamless part of life and will change the trajectory of human history, and hopefully for the better.

What does an augmented workforce look like for your industry?

Rosario B. Casas, Co-founder and CEO at XR Americas:

"The moment when we are augmenting workforce is the moment where their daily work can be converted into actionable insights, improving the KPIs (Key Performance Indicators) not only from the financials but from two other key areas: knowledge management and process ownership. It is the moment when the company can convert every action developed by an employee to generate improvement or an adjustment on the processes. It is the near real-time convergence between enterprise architecture, the Internet of things, and spatial computing, facilitated by 5G or the next generations."[94]

Future Foretold:
The World of *Minority Report*

In the visionary film *Minority Report*, Steven Spielberg presents a futuristic world that is entirely believable. Iris scanners identify passengers on a subway for security. When you walk into The Gap, the scanner recognizes you, mentions your last purchase, and recommends some new khakis that are on sale, utilizing advanced artificial intelligence algorithms. Facial and optical recognition is virtually everywhere. Personalized ads bombard you as you walk through the street. Embedded with artificial intelligence, scanners recognize your mood or state of mind and recommend products based on that information. People pay good money to enter an augmented reality arcade where they can experience skydiving, a sexual fantasy, or even murdering their boss. Each home is full of various technologies that talk to each other and are operating on voice recognition software.

The user controls their computer, which has a wall-size screen, by arm movements, tracked through enhanced cameras on the ceiling. The arm movements, reminiscent of an orchestra conductor, enable the user to perform complex manipulations of images and perform various functions with every finger through this gesture-based interface.[95] All cars are self-driving, powered by AI and maglev systems. This use of magnetic friction and power integrated into the streets has made various fuels obsolete. An eye-swapping operation is performed by a robotic machine utilizing artificial intelligence. 3-D screens or holographic videos are ubiquitous. A color newspaper is read by a man on an Ereader or foldable ePaper in the shape of a traditional newspaper, with videos, changing articles, and special announcements flowing through this wireless device (maybe utilizing 10G?). Police use jetpacks and sonic wave stun guns. Everything feels believable and familiar, yet new.

One wonders how Steven Spielberg created a world that felt so real. While it's not all here, some of it is, and the rest seems entirely possible. Simply watch the video "extras," and you'll see that Spielberg assembled dozens of respected tech experts—including futurists, architects, writers, computer scientists, biomedical researchers, and more—and asked them to paint a picture of what America will look like in 2054.[96] The production designer, Alex McDowell, kept what came to be called the "2054 bible." This 80-page guide listed aspects of the future world such as the architectural, socio-economic, political, and technological advances, and how, for instance, individual economics played into architectural forms.[97]

Sure, we may not have "Precogs" who can predict murders that can be stopped by the PreCrime unit. But almost everything else in the movie is something that scientists, engineers, biomedical researchers, computer scientists, and creatives have completed, are working on, or will be working on in the near future. In fact, one article details the fact that many of the predictions in the movie were realized thirty-five years sooner than portrayed in the film.[98][99] But what about today? Steven

Spielberg did a great job predicting the future, but we believe the future is now.

In the previous chapters, we armed you with context. We explored why businesses need to care about these new technologies. We took a trip down memory lane and investigated how we got to this point in history. And we outlined the specific six technologies that, in our opinions, form the new computing landscape—IoT, AI, the cloud, blockchain, XR, and 5G.

Now we're going to move into how these technologies are applied in different industries. Subsequent sections will also focus on specific areas, including entertainment, fashion, retail, and services. We'll go into how each industry uses technology in the new computing landscape for training, design and manufacturing, marketing and sales, collaboration, and so forth. We'll also let emerging tech voices speak for themselves.

As we explore how these keystone technologies apply to various verticals, we'll take a deep dive into how they help accelerate processes, perform tasks at scale, drive huge improvements in efficiency, and provide decision makers with crucial insight at junctions where smart choices can spur profound change.

CHAPTER FIVE

Recruiting— Augmenting Talent

As you read this, technology is reshaping nearly every industry. Yet companies are founded and run by people, and human talent remains the core business asset that ultimately drives innovation, growth, and success—at least for now. However, not all human skills, experience, and personality traits are equal when it comes to a specific job, role, or corporate culture. Additionally, the hiring process itself needs a makeover, if not a top-to-bottom overhaul.

Recruiting with AI Robots: Search and Employ

One major challenge modern corporations face is the deluge of resumes and job applications they receive. However crafty a resume or CV has been prepared, a few pages of text still constitute a very narrow lens through which hiring teams evaluate a whole person, and whether employing said person would benefit their company. HR staff have the training they need to determine whether a candidate fits a role. But they do get tired. And when they need to evaluate dozens of applicants for a single position, they are more likely to overlook critical nuances hiding in a resume.

Today, the dynamic between hiring and job-hunting runs pretty much like a chess game where applicants consciously sync their resumes with the apparent needs of a potential employer, as expressed in job ads and listings. Jobseekers write something up that sounds like what they think a hiring company wants. The trouble is, a lot of details often get lost in translation. In this environment, nearly every resume would seem like one sent by a candidate worth considering.

Using narrow and purpose-designed AI bundled into Applicant Tracking Systems (ATS) fixes this problem. The practice has become so prevalent, it may already be the mainstream solution for corporate hiring. According to some estimates, nearly all Fortune 500 companies already use AI-driven ATS to screen the flood of resumes they receive every day.[100] ATS algorithms are configured to look for specific terms or patterns in a resume that score both the skill set and overall personality of the applicant. Based on a predefined criteria, the system then recommends the best candidates. This spares the hiring manager from the arduous task of looking into every single application. For job seekers submitting via an ATS, it's now crucial that they optimize their resumes for ATS search and ranking algorithms, pad their resumes with keywords, and avoid using tables that can cause parsing errors.

The benefit applies on both sides of the equation. After all, job candidates also want to keep track of their applications. However, hiring managers and staff may not be around all the time to address the issues or answer the questions of every applicant. Fortunately, conversational AI called chatbots can provide job candidates with useful information on demand, 24/7. These low-functioning AI use Natural Language Processing (NLP) algorithms that enable the system to understand candidates' questions and respond to them over a text messaging app and other platforms. These chatbots also autonomously send alerts and notifications when an application reaches the next stage of the process.

At the same time such virtual assistants and chatbots serve job applicants, they also provide another line of defense that shields hiring managers and their companies from a flood of unqualified candidates. Further on, as the process flows forward to the interview stage, some companies use AI to analyze question-and-answer sessions and rate candidates' domain expertise, confidence, and truthfulness.

5G: Being Telepresent in the Moment

In 2012, 63 percent of HR managers conducted hiring interviews via video.[101] In April 2020, that number went up to 86 percent.[102] The global pandemic has made permanent changes for some companies who chose to close physical headquarters completely. The shift estimates that 36.2 million Americans will work remotely by 2025. That's an 87-percent increase from pre-pandemic levels.[103] Between hiring managers conducting virtual interviews and a remote workforce, network speeds and the method for interviewing needs an upgrade.

With 5G, the speed of communications goes into hyperdrive. 5G will democratize advanced communication. It also drives real-time collaboration and makes future tech, like streaming volumetric video, possible. Yes, the video interview will turn 3D with the help of 5G. Holographic interviews have been done before. Stephen Hawking appeared at the Sydney Opera House in 2015 via Cisco and the University of New South Wales, using DVE Telepresence Holographic Live Stage technology.[104]

In 2020 the NBA started using 5G for hologram interviews courtside on Turner Sports and ESPN. The NBA, working with AT&T, uses "5G to enable NBA players and analysts to interact naturally, standing or sitting, with full eye contact, as though they were physically together in the same location, talking all things NBA Playoffs and more."[105] As 5G is installed by more carriers, this type of holographic power will be available to everyone. It will replace 2D video as the go to method for communication. "As bandwidth speeds get faster, as 5G gets faster, that experience is going to become more immersive, and

I do think the opportunities will then grow for people to want to experience that and to adapt to virtual reality," said Mark Tatum, NBA Deputy Commissioner.[106]

Extended Reality: Work Like You've Already Got the Job

Some candidates and employers won't settle for interviews done over phones or web conferencing apps. For companies who want to showcase their culture, offices, and facilities to woo topnotch talent (and for applicants who seek to "have a feel" of employers' workplaces), XR technologies offer a range of ingenious solutions.

Companies now use virtual reality to provide job applicants with immersive office tours and glimpses of their corporate culture. Manufacturing plants can feature their production lines and the technical teams who run them in VR. Global brands can showcase their products and also give on-demand, experiential overviews of their operations and facilities through AR. Culture-focused employers can showcase employee wellness facilities and team dynamics on and off the workplace.

Over the past few years, many of our own clients have wanted to use VR to excite top candidates about the people, atmosphere, and spaces across their organizations. It was kind of an enhanced upgrade of the corporate videos many brands embed in their websites.

In addition to showcasing organizational culture and facilities, XR can be used in simulated field tests as well as in role auditions. Notable precedents, airlines, flight schools, and aviation companies have long used flight simulations to teach basic flight principles to new students and advanced emergency protocols for veteran pilots. Medical schools also use XR to train surgeons.[107] The same technologies can be appropriated for recruitment purposes, both for roles that require hard skills such as assembly and diagnostics, and jobs that depend on soft skills such as business negotiation. Lifting the hiring process to the next level, XR and its subfields (Augmented Reality and Virtual Reality) can be used to gauge a candidate's effectiveness at role-specific tasks.

Companies can evaluate and train candidates, presenting different mechanical parts or electronics components on a table for job applicants to interact with by tapping on a tablet or AR-enabled glasses and gesturing with their hands. Candidates' technical expertise can then be rated based on how they assemble, dissemble, fix, or handle the components, tools, machinery, and other virtual objects on the table. Using AR, recruiters acquire a fairly accurate picture on whether applicants really know what they are doing.

Meanwhile, frontline business units can leverage AR to simulate complex scenarios and assess a candidate's demeanor, skill sets, effectiveness, and overall performance amid difficult conversations or stressful conditions. These scenarios include investment pitches, mock sales, staff hiring/firing, project negotiation, and handling customer complaints.

Large companies and start-ups alike are already leveraging these technologies to great effect. In Los Angeles, a company called Talespin[108] specializes in XR and AI platforms for the enterprise. In 2019, they launched an employee termination simulator that helps companies evaluate a leader's relevant people skills for this type of situation. The scenario features near-humanlike virtual characters that react contextually and emotionally—sometimes even violently (e.g., pounding the table)—to what a subject says or does. The candidate's data for reaction time, empathy, and successful outcomes are relayed to the hiring managers for their review. Companies can even repurpose these simulations for other hiring, performance assessment, and staff promotion.

As automation replaces more and more repetitive low-skill tasks, more of the workforce will convert to information workers. These workers require a mix of domain expertise and communication skills, and companies will increasingly rely on AI and XR to help find, train, and retain them. As human resource professionals, it's important to understand not only the new knowledge and skills that these technologies require, but also the amazing potential that AI, AR, and 5G offer for identifying, attracting and retaining the best candidates.

Opportunities to Augment Recruiting

• *AI is helping recruiters and hiring managers sort through many candidates to find those with the best mix of skills and experience.*

• *AI is helping job seekers tune their applications to increase their chances of success.*

• *XR is helping companies attract better talent through campus tours, or immersive scenarios that gauge their fitness for a job.*

CHAPTER SIX

Training: Just-in-Time Help and Beyond

Next to hiring, businesses need to get new talent on board and train them to excel in the roles they have been hired for. Whether to help employees build new skills or retrain and upgrade existing ones, training programs are crucial to the sustainability of any organization. Workforce training is a recurring phase in the employment lifecycle where technology can truly make a huge difference.

What does an augmented workforce look like for your industry?

Cortney Harding, founder of Friends With Holograms:

"We think about this all day, every day. It looks like a workplace where employees are valued because their training is taken seriously. That, in turn leads to good results for employers, with lower turnover, higher satisfaction, and better productivity."[109]

Artificial Intelligence: You Missed a Spot!

Organizations use AI in many ways. In personnel development, the applications can be limitless. For example, Machine Learning algorithms can analyze training activity to detect learning gaps and improve the effectiveness of programs. AI can also assist trainees by giving dynamic recommendations in real time while they perform new tasks or solve difficult challenges. Many companies use artificial intelligence to help employees accelerate the pace and improve the impact of their training.

Stanley Black & Decker, a global manufacturing company, uses a platform from DeepHow to capture workflow data as employees perform their tasks. [110] Once the data is captured, it is extracted and synthesized using AI, known as "Stephanie." The workflows are turned into step-by-step instructional videos. Stephanie seamlessly captures and organizes expert knowledge. The AI delivers just-in-time information to workers in multiple languages, making knowledge digitalization highly efficient and scalable across the enterprise. This type of platform upskills employees. It also provides continuity for customers in spite of employee turnover. [111]

Another common way to upgrade staff training is the use of chatbots. You're probably used to chatbots deployed as a simple text chat embedded in a website, ready to answer basic questions trainees may have about their courses or workshops. But the face of chatbots is changing. Soul Machines is a company that creates digital humans. They have detailed, realistic human faces. AI empathy, compassion, and adaptability is built into their digital DNA. Being able to emotionally connect to employees leads to higher retention and completion rates. [112] At Maryville University, digital humans Mya and Emma coach students on how to fill out FAFSA applications, share information about the school's culture, and advise on academic planning. [113]

Let's say your job is to assemble a toaster. The company that hired you runs an AI program embedded in a virtual training environment built on augmented reality. Your job is to assemble an entire toaster from the different objects randomly placed on the workbench. The AR program digitally highlights which parts and tools to select first. As you assemble the toaster, the AI observes your actions. The AI might say, "Hey, it looks like you're having trouble here. Do you need help?" You can ask, "Where does the tension spring go?" or, "How do I adjust the torque on this gear?" The AI then looks through the knowledge base and answers your question based on your proficiency level. Based on your actions and questions, the system might also recommend the right training level (Beginner, Intermediate, Advanced, or Expert) and learning modules that match your needs.

AI training platforms significantly reduce the need for trainers to be physically near trainees and gives the training team more time to focus on and design better learning modules. AI trainers free up human development managers and staff to perform higher-level or strategically more important tasks while improving employee training satisfaction.

5G Technology: Giving Distance Learning New Meaning

When you have 5G's speed and throughput, computer-based training takes a quantum leap. Newly hired operators for a million-dollar printing press for example would need to spend a lot of time and exert maximum effort if they need to build competency via a two-volume manual or a thick deck of Microsoft PowerPoint slides. In contrast, a high-fidelity training simulation delivered via 5G provides immersive learning experiences that intimately connect the trainee's senses and thinking with the visual, geometric, methodological, or animated aspects of the simulation. In an instant, the trainee would know how a component looks from every angle, how it feels to operate, and how to control the machine to deliver a specific outcome.

In addition to providing high-fidelity experiences, organizations can also conduct this high-quality staff training anywhere. So instead of physically flying everyone to their headquarters for example, companies can enable all trainees to remotely observe distant manufacturing facilities from local offices, plants, or workstations at home. A past client flew hundreds of customers and personnel to Europe each year for five days of hands-on training. They would do this to familiarize people up-close with machinery, as well as to interact with expert local technicians. Covering travel, accommodation, training, and related expenses, the total cost ran at around one million dollars per year. With remote digital training delivered via high-speed broadband or 5G, companies can now bring everybody to the same location virtually. Only this time, they do so with far less expense and logistical hassle. Moreover, they can achieve similar or even better learning outcomes as compared to physically transporting their teams to the training venue.

While seemingly low-key compared to its affiliated technologies, 5G helps address urgent issues that are reshaping the future of the planet. As the reality of climate change looms, air travel—and its ecosystem of businesses and customers—has had its share of carbon-shaming. In addition, the likelihood of another pandemic similar to the one that wreaked havoc in 2020 remains high. Addressing both challenges, the case for remote work, collaboration, and training could be no less than imperative. Which of course, makes a rock-solid case for faster connectivity with 5G wireless networking.

Extended Reality: On the Job Training, Virtually

The training applications of extended reality (XR) are multifaceted, with high-fidelity and enhanced simulations the most obvious. Across the board, XR simulations enable companies to improve training effectiveness, learner safety, and worker performance.

If you need to learn how to use a hay baler, a drill press, or other kinds of hazardous equipment for example, XR simulations can make it safer, faster, and easier to develop proficiency. You can train how to operate, fix, or manage virtually any machine in any type of scenario—troubleshoot in low-light conditions, replace a worn-out component, or configure machine settings to generate a specific output. While doing so, companies and their trainees get the added benefit of eliminating safety hazards and the likelihood of damaging or breaking real equipment.

New York City's rail system (which ranks among the planet's largest) moves nearly nine million people per day.[114] The subway management regularly replaces old train cars with new ones. But the system retains its ancient network of tracks, switches, and stops which mostly date back to the 1930s! Given its antiquated infrastructure, the subway requires an army of technicians to keep it running safely and dependably.

Training a new batch of rail technicians always comes as a huge challenge for management. Millions of commuters depend daily on the train system. An entire metropolitan area can't be told that the subway is closed until further notice. So the trainers teach new technicians using the few remaining pieces of equipment they still have that are not in service. Given the hazardous conditions, the trainer team puts safety as the top priority of their training program.

Traditional training like this can be dull, ineffective, and time-consuming. Everybody may just stand around getting a few glimpses of the rare equipment. At the early stages, trainees are lucky to even touch and manipulate the machines, which are made up largely of greasy cast iron weighing several hundred pounds.

Considering all these instructional challenges, new technicians must be trained for a year before they can safely work on the tracks. Plus, they need another two years of apprenticeship to become full-fledged railway technicians. Meanwhile, HR still needs to keep a number of retirees around for their arcane knowledge that needs to be shared with the next generation of workers.

VR/AR gives every trainee a highly immersive and hands-on experience with a digital 3D copy of the rare equipment, right off the bat. Moreover, any type of difficult scenario can be simulated as often as needed to reinforce concepts, protocols, and skills. XR simulations allow for greater depth and speed of training than traditional methods.

Diversity, inclusion, and sexual-harassment training is especially difficult because you're asking someone to try to see the world from a different viewpoint instead of simply learning a new task. Companies like VR Perspectives aim to alleviate the challenge through virtual reality. VR Perspectives founder Myra LalDin says that that diversity training is for everyone. Where some diversity and inclusion training may single people out for being wrong, VR Perspectives doesn't include any such commentary. Myra said in VR, "You go in and learn on your own, and come to your own conclusions. With learning tools and facilitated discussions, you learn from one another, and create the culture you want from your firsthand experience."[115]

Overall, XR solves quite a lot of (but not all) training challenges. Mostly, it takes much of the drudgery out of the learning process, collects data that's useful to identify needs or gaps, and distributes training more cheaply and easily. It also gives more time for experts and managers to focus on making things better.

The Internet of Things:
The Connected Workplace

Door locks, thermostats, electric lights, and home appliances rarely generate much excitement. The Internet of Things has changed that. Mundane electronic devices now link together in a network where useful information about and around them are shared. This has led to the rise of smart homes, vehicles, factories, and other stuff that figured only in science fiction a couple decades ago. According to IoT leader Ericsson, around 25 billion IoT devices will connect to the network by 2025.[116]

In the field of training, IoT applications are limitless. One common use case involves the IoT-enabling technology called Near Field Communication (NFC). Zebra Technologies is a fifty-year old company that provides a wide range of printing, tracking, and labeling solutions. The company has been building and selling NFC chips to enterprise customers from the retail, manufacturing, logistics, healthcare, government, and other industries.[117]

One of Zebra's clients needed to contain—if not eliminate—potentially fatal fall hazards for maintenance crews working in airports and other facilities. Depending on their specializations, some aviation maintenance crews clean, paint, repair, and conduct quality checks on the airplane's fuselage, wings, and the rudders and stabilizers on its tail. In many airliners, the top of the tail fin can be taller than fifty-five feet, or slightly taller than a five-story building. Falls from that elevation are likely to be deadly or crippling.

Working on this vertical stabilizer tail fin requires an aerial work platform, usually a scissor lift, with crews obliged to strap on a safety harness and secure it to the platform. But people being people, they sometimes forget protocol. While one safety failure is a tragic accident, multiple and recurrent failures could put a company out of business.

To address these hazards, Zebra added NFC labels to safety harnesses, personal protective gear, and other health and safety equipment. For this client, Zebra designed a system of protocols, sensors, and labels, wherein an NFC label is attached to the carabiner of a safety harness and an NFC "reader" attached to the part where workers clip in the harness. The system follows a safety protocol that ensures work sequences occur in a specific way. Any deviation from the predefined sequences will trigger an alarm or override/halt the process. This way, when a maintenance crew forgets to clip in their safety harness (i.e., the corresponding NFC labels aren't aligned or not transmitting the right radio signals), the scissor lift won't raise the aerial work platform and a safety warning alarm will be triggered. This solution allowed Zebra's client to cut accidents of this type to zero, saving many lives and protecting productivity.

At Friends With Holograms, Cortney Harding (founder and CEO), is at the forefront of using VR/AR for employee training. In her own words:

> We've built several VR training pieces focused on soft skills, and are starting to play in the collaborative VR space as well. Our piece for Accenture, AvenueS, was named Best VR/AR at Mobile World Congress and was also a finalist for an SXSW Innovation Award. Several states are utilizing it. In Indiana, they reported an 18 percent decrease in caseworker turnover after using it.[118]

Ario Technologies is known for combining the power of scalable web and mobile technologies with augmented reality. In early 2020, this AR SaaS company was named the winner of Verizon's Built on 5G Challenge. Granted a partnership, they began working with Verizon's 5G network and preparing Ario's AR tools for the future of network connectivity. A few of the most significant gains that 5G will bring to this industry are the ability to utilize mobile edge computing (MEC), significantly reduced latency, and faster download and upload speeds. The ability to move processes from the cloud to the edge will reduce the number of hops required that might have resulted in 100ms or more for application connectivity. This directly reduces the latency that would continue to exist if not for 5G.

The co-founder of Ario, Nate Fender, states:

> With increased data speeds, it's now realistic to load large amounts of data in the background of mobile applications. It creates the possibility of on-demand AR Cloud maps, larger trained machine learning models, and interactive 3D experiences that wouldn't have otherwise been possible. 5G has the potential to truly bring that type of seamless experience to life for the digitally connected worker.[119]

Regarding training, Fender told us:

There's magnificent potential for symbiosis between machine learning and augmented reality. Specifically, collected imagery can be trained for a visual search engine and directly applied to spatial interaction. Within the industrial enterprise landscape, there's a mountain of legacy equipment that digitally connected workers must maintain for the foreseeable future. Now, imagine approaching any piece of equipment as a technician and instantly detecting the make/model of the equipment and downloading a pre-built AR Cloud model specific to that location. There is an immediate increase in situational awareness, and information is presented in a way that is personalized to the worker's learning strengths, whether it be 3D models, videos and / or images.

Utilizing AI and AR technologies, Ario users will be able to perform key tasks in unprecedented ways, increasing efficiency, accuracy, and capabilities.

Fender has many concerns with the landscape of manufacturing and workforce changes, but believes that XR can provide solutions:

With millions of manufacturing jobs not being filled over the next several years and more than a third of the utilities' workforce becoming eligible for retirement, we see a significant skills gap. That gap is the difference between those with 20+ years of experience and those who just entered the workforce. We are seeing spatial computing deployed in both training and production environments. With highly repeatable and preventative maintenance procedures being conducted on a regular basis by a changing variable of frontline workers, spatial computing is seen as a bridge between those with little experience and a highly complex procedure. In manufacturing, changing a production line over to output a new variant of a product happens somewhat regularly. Spatial context is critical when steps in changeover procedures take place at different areas on a line.

Sophia Moshasha, is the former Head of Partnerships at Brightline Interactive and the Vice President of the Washington DC chapter of VR/AR Association. When we asked her how artificial intelligence is being used in her industry, she said:

Brightline Interactive is using VR combined with brain computer interface (BCI) and AI to drive autonomous and personalized training experiences. Brightline's solution, the Performance Adaptive Virtual Engine (PAVE), combines a variety of sensor arrays to assess active and passive reactions within simulation and adapts occurrences within the training environment to detect and target trainee-specific proficiencies and deficiencies. The methodologies of PAVE can transfer to training in various industries but also in the workplace to deliver content based on user needs and interactions.

VR/AR will be the true testbed for proving the power of 5G to the consumer market in particular. With VR/AR there will be a demonstrable way to show that 5G is not just for faster data transfer on cell phones, but allows access to information, spatially, in a way that was not possible before 5G.[120]

Utilizing training via AR will become more and more indispensable as industries become more complex and change at a faster rate. How are you going to train people who don't have access to a facility? How will you train people on new equipment when a mentor can't stand by their side in person? VR and AR training has proven to be exponentially more effective than reading a manual or watching videos, so companies would be wise to invest in VR headsets for their employees. For this reason alone, wise companies will invest in AR technologies.

Opportunities to Augment Training

• *AI is adapting training to different learners, suggesting new content or presenting it as their unique learning styles require.*

• *XR is safely empowering trainees through dynamic, immersive training that sticks through consistency and repetition.*

• *5G is giving trainees more impactful experiences whether they're in the office or remote.*

CHAPTER SEVEN

Research and Development: Chasing the Future

AI is providing breakthroughs in R&D. As pointed out by Roger Spitz, researchers used AI to design a new drug called Halicin, which kills off many strains of bacteria. Additionally, AI recently played a prominent role with a new OCD medication called DSP-1181, which was the first non-human made drug molecule to enter phase 1 clinical trials. Imagine using dozens of AI computers to search for a vaccine for the coronavirus. With intelligence that far surpasses human intelligence, a solution could be found in record time.

At a 2017 seminar, University of Toronto Professor Avi Goldfarb, explained how AI is a General Purpose Technology. Goldfarb said, "the economic value of the Internet revolution can be described as reducing the cost of communications and of search, thus enabling us to easily find and access all kinds of information." The professor feels that AI's economic impact can be seen in its cost reductions when used at scale, but that R&D offers an even more fundamental opportunity. He said AI "may have an even larger impact on the economy by serving as a new general-purpose method of invention that can reshape the nature of the innovation process and the organization of R&D." The authors argue that AI—and deep learning in particular—is actually a new kind of research tool which will open up new avenues of inquiry across a broad set of domains—an invention of a method of inventing. Such inventions not only reduce the costs of specific innovation activities, but actually enable a new approach to innovation itself, "altering the playbook in the domains where the new tools are applied."[121]

What does an augmented workforce look like for your industry?

Julie Smithson, co-founder of MetaVRse shared:

"An augmented workforce is having a digital implementation of assistance, guidance, and visualization to support communications with employees and customers."[122]

Following over thirty years at Ford Motor Company, Elizabeth Baron was an Immersive Innovation Technical Fellow at Silverdraft Supercomputing. Silverdraft focuses on the use of unique supercomputing architecture to address the significant computational and processing needs of high-end rendering, VR, visual effects, and visualization.

Elizabeth told us that, "AI is key for the emotive and scientific visualization in automotive. It allows for experiential analysis, to understand the design and performance of an automotive system in an immersive, holistic environment, with intelligent information presented in context. Cars are learning by experience." Regarding AR, she states, "Immersive realities are used to experience design, engineering and manufacturing data in a way that everyone understands because it's based on the solid engineering and design created within enterprise." But, 5G will bring AI and AR together. "5G will revolutionize automotive. Not only for use of low-latency, multi-sensory

VR in the cloud for product development, but also for driverless cars and smart cities!"[123]

In the Pharmacology industry, researchers are using Artificial Intelligence to discover new areas to research. They're leveraging Natural Language Processing (NLP) to scour thousands of scientific research articles[124], looking for interesting research to take further.

In many cases, the value of AI shows up when viewed through the lens of work at massive scale. In the research field, AI is becoming a vital tool in finding the right opportunities, working deeply to find solutions, and in testing those theories towards greater benefit.

Across industries, R&D teams are using AI and AR to collect, organize, and understand data. They are applying these findings to develop exciting new designs that are safer, more effective, and more cost-efficient than those created with traditional technologies. How will you disrupt your own company's research activities? Here are some suggestions:

Opportunities to Augment Research and Development

• *AI is being used to scour research for opportunities for deeper work.*

• *AI is being used by researchers to iterate much more quickly and safely than doing traditional trials or testing.*

• *XR is allowing researchers to collaborate remotely on virtual models.*

• *5G is bringing researchers together in more places and across more devices.*

CHAPTER EIGHT

Design and Manufacturing: *Actually* Building a Better Tomorrow

The potential of a machine to become "human" remains one of the most intriguing aspects of technology, a concept often explored in science fiction and widely anticipated by some of today's leading thinkers.[125] Over the years in fact, a few AI systems (such as Google's Duplex AI[126]) have allegedly passed the fabled Turing Test, a method developed in 1950 for determining whether a computer exhibits human-like behavior. While many such claims almost always happen amid a cloud of controversy,[127] the mere ability of today's chatbots to sustain rudimentary conversations with humans already points to a future similar to those depicted in movies such as *Her, I, Robot,* and *Iron Man* (J.A.R.V.I.S not Ultron).

What does an augmented workforce look like for your industry?

Sophia Moshasha, Vice President of the Washington DC chapter of the VR/AR Association:

"The idea of an augmented workforce is to have targeted information delivered, in the context that makes the most sense at the right time and within a medium that doesn't interrupt the current task but perhaps, enhances it. With an augmented workforce, organizations can cut back on overhead costs, give employees an engaging and enriched experience, and increase in efficiency and productivity in the workplace."[128]

Today, neural networks replicate some functions that were formerly considered the exclusive domain of humans. By crunching extremely large datasets and performing trial-and-error millions of times in a single cycle, advanced "deep learning" algorithms can re-imagine, design, and create an extensive assortment of products.

They're not as good as the finest human practitioners yet, but the fascinating race has begun. Then again, aesthetics is one thing. Practicality is another. Any business will readily embrace a technology that can improve, streamline, or accelerate its design and production processes. Now these techniques are being applied to create stronger bridges, more efficient buildings, and to diagnose, anticipate, and even prevent costly repairs. And here are several ways new technologies are changing how companies conceptualize and fabricate the trappings of modern life.

Artificial Intelligence: Invention is 99.999999% (Digital) Perspiration

We have taught machines to create art,[129] make music,[130] and write poems[131]. When we use artificial intelligence, we literally share control of the creative process with a computer. We allow powerful algorithms to virtually build an infinite number of iterations for a single product. To harness this new creative process, companies need to establish the rule set and tolerances within which the AI can operate.

Construction firms configure AI to use a specific type and amount of concrete for a given project. Engineers set the number of floors for an algorithm to simulate the impact of earthquakes, fires, and vent heat on the structural integrity and safety of the building. AI can quickly generate tens of millions of design iterations that conform to the rules and let humans select the best variant based on aesthetics or some higher level criteria. Artificial intelligence helps us build safer buildings that use less materials and take less time to complete.

This AI-powered "generative" design approach doesn't build things the way humans do. AI designs unusual and stunning structures that remain compliant with safety standards and other predefined parameters. Machine learning performs all the heavy lifting required to virtually build countless design permutations and shortlist the ones that might appeal most to humans. Often, generative design helps decision makers determine the feasibility of a particular design based on specific parameters for quality, effectiveness, durability, cost/time of production, environmental impact, marketability, and other cost-benefit factors

Next-gen technologies augment the creative capabilities of humans without fully usurping our central role in economic, artistic, and cultural production. Although we have the ability to detect deviations from a pattern, we're not always great at identifying the source or cause of the deviation and how to fix it. This is where AI comes in handy.

Email services like Google's Gmail and Microsoft's Outlook incorporate AI that predicts your sentences as you type to save time writing emails. The same thing is happening to CAD software. By studying millions of designs, machine learning predicts what shapes or objects someone will place next.[132] AI-powered CAD software learns and adjusts on the fly based on the customer account or product being built. This saves engineers time, computing cost, and passes on those benefits to the customer.

Within a plant, AI can "see" into the future how a manufacturing line will run in a week, month, or year from now.[133] Sensors in the plant talk in real time to the digital twin. This gives manufacturers the ability to see which components are starting to fail or upcoming maintenance will be scheduled. This will allow them to plan around important or abnormal orders.

We can train computers to automatically detect, diagnose, and fix deviations. Through machine learning, AI can be trained to diagnose and categorize equipment based on how they sound: running smoothly, sputtering, or broken. Factories are using AI to monitor and fix equipment such as automated manufacturing robots. AI programmed for preventive maintenance gives recommendations on whether a cooling fan needs repair or which date lubricants need to be flushed and replenished. For offices, such AI can be packaged as mobile apps. You just need to hold your phone next to a defective photocopier so it can "listen" to the machine. It can tell you what's needed and maybe even explain how to fix it yourself.

Virtual Prototypes, Real Results

Companies spend time, effort, and money to build a product or provide a service. These are generally accepted business expenses. But in some lines of business, the mere presentation of a proposed project or proof of concept nearly costs the same as producing and selling an actual product.

In one example, a global manufacturing firm spent almost the same amount of time and money to get a product tested and evaluated by its internal teams and customers as they spent on actual manufacturing and distribution.

Because the client has a brand to protect, they went to great lengths to have product ideas prototyped, sampled, and critiqued by staff and customers before the company manufactured its finished goods for consumers. At the end of the day, they spent a massive amount of money on getting everything right before going to market.

Consequently, there's a lot of waste, a lot of iterations in the design phase, and serious security risks which arise from sharing prototypes and other sensitive information to various people before releasing a product. When it comes to this aspect, this company simply lacked the ability and the tools to achieve maximum efficiency as an enterprise.

Fortunately, they're now using a combination of 5G technology and XR. Their teams make digital 3D versions of goods that people can see and interact with. Executives and partners across the supply chain, as well as potential customers, examine the simulated products from any angle and experiment with different components and variants of the product. The company no longer needs to ship a physical product to diverse locations to facilitate simultaneous review and approval. Via high-speed Internet or 5G, team members from anywhere in the world participate in the live, virtual process and collaborate in making the product better. Anyone can say, "What if we relocate this feature on the back?" Or, "What if we use this cool material instead?" Based on the participants' requests, the product is iterated in real-time and in countless ways. This type of focused, high-bandwidth application helps sustain the value of an immersive experience and the digital models of the product are used not only for engineering and manufacturing, but for marketing as well.

5G and XR have taken this company's process through an aggressive and game-changing transformation. Innovative companies are spending less, they're getting results more quickly, and they're securing their intellectual property. For the enterprise, these futuristic technologies are powerful solutions to solve today's problems.

Product designers use XR platforms like the NVIDIA Holodeck to work on models in a simulated real-word environment. In XR, designers collaborate in real-time with their peers to validate materials and model proportions of a product. NVIDIA Holodeck "brings designers, peers, and stakeholders together from anywhere in the world to build and explore creations in a highly realistic, collaborative, and physically simulated VR environment."[134] NVIDIA Holodeck is entirely in virtual reality, allowing for real-time collaboration on assets that might not be fully developed yet in real life. Working in VR this way reduced prototyping errors because designers walk around and products at a one-to-one scale.[135] Realistic VR designs make it easy for non-technical people to review products. They don't have to understand CAD software or try to envision what the product will look like at scale because they see it at scale in VR.

XR and the 5G connected plant improves employee safety. The plant is an orchestra of moving parts, machines, and humans. While there are safety guidelines, it's not always clear where it's best for a human to be. Connected cameras don't always catch the nuances in the plant but Internet-enabled sensors that talk to a XR headset keep people safe. It doesn't have to be a headset. Sensors send notifications to an operator's smartphone or smartwatch that vibrates on their arm, warning them of an unsafe situation. XR and connected devices are about empowering the worker. It's about getting the right information to the right person, at the right time, and on the right device. It's not about the worker going to the information. It's about the information coming to the worker.[136]

James Ashley is the CTO of LifeMap and the former 3D Development Lead at VIMaec, a leading building information modeling firm. He told us that "AI is being used to analyze the construction materials being used in residential and commercial construction in order to determine trends and guide vendor strategy. One of the particular issues facing 3D architectural visualization is reconstructing useful plans from 3D point clouds of older buildings. Machine learning is one of the key tools many are looking toward in order to solve this problem." Ashley explains that architects need to be able to visualize full buildings from 2D blueprints. However, very few people can actually do this accurately."[137]

Ashley continues, "The construction of a modern office building is probably one of the most complicated coordinated tasks that human beings organize themselves to complete. It's lots of people coming together with huge budgets and short timelines to get something done following a vision that few can actually understand. Spatial computing is the missing piece that can help identify inefficiencies and provide cost savings to this enormous task." Because architectural visualizations tend to require a massive amount of data, they will need something like 5G in order to make it generally usable in the architecture, engineering, and construction (AEC) industry. Ashley believes that 5G "will accelerate our ability to bring life-size digital models of a building to the construction site and help guide the construction process." But Ashley shared one caution:

Construction is an old technology—one of the oldest. Knowledge of how to do it is still passed on through a journeyman process, sometimes literally from parent-to-child. The challenge of introducing emerging tech to what is ultimately a wisdom-based technology (architecture, drafting, bricklaying, etc.) is to improve it without breaking it. We must preserve what is rich and wonderful about AEC while fixing the things that do not, or no longer, work well. This is always the danger and the promise of introducing emerging tech to our world. We have to be vigilant about not breaking what is already there.

As the population grows, the need for AI, AR, and XR will increase because of its ability to visualize designs and tailor product interaction on the fly. Countless industries are already reaping the rewards of engaging their customers with as many senses as possible.

Opportunities to Augment Design and Manufacturing

• Design engineers can use AI (generative design) to create parts and products that are stronger, safer, and more cost-efficient.

• Designs can be stress-tested in simulations to achieve better results faster and more safely.

• Engineers can leverage XR for design collaboration, testing, and training.

• Fast networking with 5G is allowing for greater real-time collaboration across a range of locations and devices.

CHAPTER NINE

Marketing and Sales: Augmenting the Grand Bazaar

Among the most tech-forward fields in business, marketing and sales are harnessing the tremendous potential of AI, XR, 5G, and other technologies. One of the most distinct areas is digital advertising, which traces its roots back to the dotcom era when web pages started becoming valuable real estate for ads. Over the years, terms like *cost-per-click* and *retargeting* became buzzwords as dominant players refined the ad-serving process using AI-powered media-buying and recommendation algorithms. Now, marketers and brands are preparing for life after flat, interruptive marketing. Lisi Linares, founder of LINARES PR+, predicts that as AI/AR and 5G are broadly implemented, "the world will be almost unrecognizable, overnight, not unlike when electricity, cinema, telephone, or the phonograph came on the scene. VR/AR will be a household and business staple, whether in education, training, or entertainment. It is inescapable."[138]

Artificial Intelligence

Algorithms can be refined to process any other data that have potential value to users. For example, the same system can be made to talk with traffic control sensors and the systems of other food retailers in the area so that when a traffic jam occurs along the detour, AI can recommend alternate fresh food retailers that also offer attractive discounts. Sales and marketers can establish brand presence in this new space by giving customer AI systems access to their menu, service listings, and other data; and by offering attractive callouts such as coupons, early-bird discounts, and other marketing tools.

Through programmatic advertising and retargeting, ad networks gather data on users' online behavior and use algorithms to sell and deliver targeted ads that they're more likely to click, based on what they've clicked before. The algorithm looks at all the data of everything anyone has ever watched, read, or clicked, then tries to serve similar, relevant, or associated offerings. Think of the process as some form of collaborative filtering between brands and users, both of whom benefit when product recommendations become more relevant. Today, AI powers the buying and selling of these targeted audiences, massively increasing the scope of its usage across platforms.

So, while brands have been using technology to advertise for a few decades, newer technologies have radically enhanced both the user experience and the business benefit of digital marketing. Chatbots, for example, allow users to directly interact with a brand, whether in asking questions about a product or performing a specific task. Today, just about every industry, from airlines[139] to banks,[140] uses conversational bots to assist human marketers, sellers, and customer care specialists.

Chatbots themselves have evolved from simple text-based programs to popular virtual assistants (like Alexa, Google Assistant, and Siri) that have voice-recognition capabilities. Some have even gone further. Autodesk, for example, initially partnered with IBM to create an AI-powered chatbot named Ava.[141] The engineering-focused software company then worked with Soul Machines to enable Ava to "see, hear, and convey" human emotions. Combined with a photorealistic and visually captivating persona, Ava interacts with Autodesk users to effectively address their concerns using virtual empathy.

Designing AI-powered digital humans require personas, digital conversationalist review, and optimization to match the brand they will represent. This will fall to the marketing department. If they choose to work with Soul Machines, they will use the Digital DNA™ Studio (DDNA Studio) to design the way their digital people look, speak, and empathize. Digital humans go beyond simple AI chatbots. They grow and evolve over time to provide real value to their customers. But that value can only come if the people behind them define clear roles and compelling values for their digital teammates.

Marketing departments use artificial intelligence to reduce cost and time of commercial shoots. Synthesia, an artificial intelligence, and video synthesis company, uses AI to transcreate ads for different regions. A company can shoot a commercial one time. The AI swaps out logos, changes words, and even manipulates people's mouths to match the new words. Global production company Craft Worldwide used Synthesia's AI technology in a JustEat commercial. They filmed a commercial for JustEat one time, then used Synthesia to transcreate the ad for their MenuLog brand.[142]

Alan Smithson thinks the film *Minority Report* is predictive. AI will analyze our body language in order to enhance marketing and advertising. Smithson told us, "AI is being used in everything from computer vision allowing complex 3D scenes and elements to be created from a few photographs to machine-learning algorithms learning about the environments we are in to give us persistent, multi-user experiences. Collecting data from head pose, heart rate, gait, eye tracking, and hand tracking, will allow us to create hyper-personalized, contextualized experiences."[143] AI will perform the lion's share of marketing and sales and with more accurate targeting. What salesperson can know which product to share with a client based on their heart rate, and analyze a wealth of other information to come up with a personalized solution in the blink of an eye?

5G and XR: Right Before
Our Very Eyes

Given 5G's higher bandwidth, businesses can create and sustain highly immersive virtual experiences to its internal teams, partners, and customers. Among many other applications, 5G raises buying and selling to an entirely new level. Ample bandwidth and near instantaneous transmission speeds enable brands to deliver immersive, high-definition experiences with practically zero latency. For both end-product consumers and enterprise buyers, that means never needing to physically visit a brick-and-mortar store to meticulously examine, try out, and buy a product.

Virtual stores powered by a combination of 5G and XR enable consumers to "hold" and "manipulate" products, "wear" a pair of shoes, and "see" whether a jacket perfectly fits their frame or whether it complements their other accessories and gadgets. Companies like Obsess turn company storefronts into virtual showrooms that immerse brands in the buyer experience.[144] Augmented reality can bring a volumetric capture of a product right into a customer's living room, not just a 3D model.

Marketing and sales are no longer regulated to humans. Virtual beings, digital influencers, and holographic models are entering the marketing department. Digital humans build relationships with consumers. Marketing departments have more control over their brand's image when creating their own digital influencers, but they still maintain a sense of authenticity. Gen Z is already interesting with digital influencers like Lil Miquela on Instagram. When they graduate to the workforce, they will expect to continue working with virtual beings.

Many customers gravitate towards brands that launch clever uses of next-gen technologies. After all, customer experience is a new currency—especially in a flipped economy where customers control the conversation. In this new normal, brands that adopt these new technologies early in the game achieve more than an entry point: they gain mindshare among their target audiences.

Through configurators (also called customization engines), high-end websites have adopted early versions of AR technology. Their use is rapidly gaining widespread acceptance, with the automotive industry among the most aggressive adopters. If you want to buy a sports car for example, you can configure it to your personal preferences (and budget) online by using an AR app. No need to visit the nearest dealer.

If you say, "I want red leather seats, tinted windows, and skylights." One of these apps just records your personal settings and sends them to all the dealers in your area. You'll get an alert if dealers already have a unit in stock which meets all your preferences. Otherwise, you can tell the specific dealer you prefer how soon you'll need the vehicle.

The configurator provides customization options for trims, body color, interior, and other variables with corresponding prices. Such convenience benefits both buyer and seller. In fact, around 90 percent of car sales for a particular car brand were made using a configurator, with buyers never setting foot in a dealership.

In 2017, John led the creation of Porsche's first AR-driven configurator app,[145] and the results were amazing. The iPhone app enabled the German carmaker to be the only brand at the time to provide customers with the ability to create and examine photorealistic 3D rendering[146] of their dream car in the real world—just by pulling up their iPhones, anytime and anywhere. Work has continued since their early lead and they've made beautiful progress.[147]

At the same time as the AR app hooked customers, it also provided valuable data to Porsche's sales and marketing teams. User engagement with the app helped generate information about which options most consumers were interested in—from model preferences to color. Such insights help automakers substantially improve efficiency and margins by reducing production waste while selling more units faster.

This type of AR application helps companies shorten their sales cycles while acquiring business intelligence about their customers. As an example, in Porsche's case, having insights into which body colors are most popular and in which proportions not only enables dealers to sell cars faster. It also allows the purchasing department to make efficient orders of paints based on actual color popularity among customers.

Additionally, sustained usage of the AR app keeps Porsche updated about changing consumer preferences in real time (favorite colors and features come and go). They won't be surprised when blue suddenly becomes in fashion and they'll have ample blue units in inventory to quickly monetize the opportunity. Otherwise, they can get blindsided by whimsical consumer trends and realize that they don't have enough burgundy paint at the moment to meet a feverish, but short-lived, trend. For high-end brands, this could translate to millions of dollars in lost opportunity.

Sales thrive on market insights, and businesses can't afford to ignore the new breed of data-mining tools now available. Apps driven by next-gen technologies give brands the ability to explore consumer sentiment, behavior, and choice. In turn, this empowers companies to predict demand more accurately, produce efficiently, sell more products faster, and remain responsive to evolving consumer desires and needs.

"AR is transforming marketing," said Dr. Joachim Scholz, a marketing professor at Brock University. "Augmented reality has found a strong use case in moving customers through the decision journey because it adds value from consideration over evaluation to purchase. Yet, we may find the even greater potential of AR when looking beyond the funnel and asking ourselves how consumers spend their day-to-day lives. Augmented reality can turn products into owned media channels inside consumers' homes, deepen consumer/brand relationships, celebrate consumer tribes, and create entirely new brand storyscapes. Marketers can use AR to trigger word-of-mouth and enchant consumption experiences."[148] AR's current appeal may be its novelty, but in the future, the engaging experience will likely make other, less-immersive experiences obsolete.

In the world of retail design, emerging tech is taking hold. Major retailers are using VR to design their stores. Our predictions aren't academic. Once in 2020, John learned of a leading U.S. retailer redesigning their stores in virtual reality. They invited a few dozen stakeholders into a virtual space using VR headsets. Everyone could walk through an aisle together (try doing that in person with fifty people). They moved the lights around, changed product displays, and brainstormed together on other parts of the space. In the past, the company would fly fifty people to a particular city to work on this project in a physical space, all at great expense (think of the cost for the flights, hotel, food, stipends, and more for so many people).

The stakeholders all said this VR experience was so impressive that they couldn't imagine going back to the way they used to do it. Designing a future store exclusively in virtual reality is something that companies may have eventually gotten to, but the pandemic has accelerated this.

Early Augmenters: Marketing with XR

There are a number of people in the XR for marketing community educating others about the business potential of XR and other exponential technologies. Here are a few brief introductions that could help you stay in touch with the latest developments in this exciting area:

Alan Smithson is the CEO of MetaVRse (@AlanSmithson1 on Twitter). His company offers a 3D/XR platform that allows creators to design solutions for industries such as marketing, retail, training, healthcare, engineering, and education. He had his "a-ha moment" the first time he tried VR. "I realized that this was the future of human communication. With that lens, you start to realize the true potential of a new medium. From photogrammetry quickly capturing people, places, and things into photorealistic 3D models to XR collaboration tools that allow people to design, train, sell and communicate in a more visceral way, XR is creating real value for organizations right now. Augmentation will give humans something similar to superpowers. It allows for our physical bodies to do the impossible, making us super-human."[149]

Smithson stated that XR technologies are predicted to create over one-trillion dollars in enterprise value in the next ten years. And, he has seen how XR has led to a 70-percent increase in retention rates in training, a 100-percent increase in visual attention, a 90-percent reduction in training costs and time, and 25-percent higher conversion rates in sales. He recognizes that some people will object stubbornly to wearing XR glasses. However, a digital contact lens or a moveable headset could be a possibility. Yet, Smithson challenges us to forget about logistics surrounding wearing glasses, "and instead focus on the question 'What can we do with the technology that exists today?' We can begin to develop solutions to problems that become standard, and this will lead to applications that we use regularly enough to warrant wearing glasses all day long." Skeptics may push back against that, but Smithson protests this as well: "Try going a day without your phone or computer or simply put your device on airplane mode. In this sense, we are already living in an augmented workforce."

Many companies are using AR and spatial computing to give buyers a physical product experience through digital while shopping from the comfort of their own home. Ashley Crowder, co-founder and CEO of VNTANA, is on a mission to help companies easily create 3D web and AR experiences at scale, helping large companies with many SKUs create, manage, and distribute 3D at scale. She has witnessed how these technologies have increased sales and customer satisfaction. "Our clients see enormous value in the 3D visualization, particularly in testing fit with furniture and appliances using AR. 3D is proven to increase online sales while decreasing returns." However, due to the enormous amount of data that is needed for such interactions, Crowder knows that 5G will lead to great possibilities: "5G is helping us create higher fidelity 3D web and AR experiences all housed in our cloud-based CMS.

This allows us to send 3D assets dynamically in AR, VR, and 3D on the web."[150]

Alex Goldberg, the XR Subject Matter Expert at REI (Recreational Equipment Inc.), is helping customers with their purchases through AR. In Goldberg's own words:

> With the aid of Augmented Reality, REI can display a full-scale version of many of our products to our customers that are shopping with a phone or tablet. With the AR capabilities currently offered, we are now enabling our customers to closely examine, and even walk inside of a highly detailed digital twin version of a tent, all while shopping at home on their mobile device.[151]

Samantha G. Wolfe (@samanthagwolfe on Twitter) is the founder of PitchFWD and co-author of *Marketing New Realities: An Introduction to Virtual Reality & Augmented Reality Marketing, Branding, & Communications*. She explains that "AI and Machine Learning are used mainly to accelerate the impact of AR and VR technologies. They allow new worlds to become more seamless with the real world."[152] This can be useful for trying on clothing before purchasing, shopping for furniture and visualizing new pieces in your home, or taking a campus tour.

Navah Berg (@navahk on Twitter) is a Social VR communications professional. She has seen how AR has increased sales for fashion companies. "Augmented Reality in Social will continue to push boundaries and be used in ways to make content interactive and come alive," Berg told us. "A great example in the fashion world is [the British fashion brand] ASOS and the AR tool they used to showcase their product called 'See My Fit.' It allows digital mapping of a product on a model in different sizes and on different body types. This gives the customer more confidence to purchase."[153]

Alice Delahunt, Chief Digital Officer at Ralph Lauren, is one of the most visionary and forward-thinking leaders in the fashion industry today. She worked on digital, augmented reality campaigns for Ralph Lauren. In 2020, Ralph Lauren partnered with SnapChat and Bitmoji. The goal was to disrupt the way Ralph Lauren told their story to younger consumers. It was reported that 10 million people used the Ralph Lauren Bitmoji clothing. Bitmoji users tried on some 250 million pieces of digital apparel from the collection.[154] Ralph Lauren continued to push the innovation when they turned their logo into a scannable experience. Snap users can scan any Ralph Lauren logo on SnapChat, whether on a polo shirt or a website, to unlock an augmented reality experience. The Ralph Lauren digital team updates the experience throughout the year to match the current season. Ralph's move into augmented reality shows how brands should leverage partnerships to use the immersive tools available.

Across industries, the arrival of these new technologies offers a reset, just as previous general-purpose technologies like the Internet and Mobile have. The companies that seize the opportunity to improve their customer experience with these technologies have a chance to grab more market share and succeed in the near, and possibly long term.

Opportunities to Augment Marketing and Sales

• *AI chatbots are helping customers make choices and solve problems.*

• *AR allows customers to take product tours, peruse configured options, and explore virtual try-ons for greater confidence in purchasing.*

• *VR is helping customers come together to experience branded environments and products when they can't visit retail locations.*

• *5G is helping customers have richer experiences in more places and on more devices.*

CHAPTER TEN

Collaboration: We Won't Call it Virtual for Long

We live in a time where productivity software is no longer enough for satisfactory team collaboration and communication. In this time of working from home and beyond, we need intelligent technology to speed up decision making (slowed down by new-to-remote work teams) and bring back employee satisfaction. This is where teams can leverage artificial intelligence to make remote work more engaging.

AI Collaboration

Voice transcription software counts among the most notable technologies that continue to impact education, training, and collaboration among individuals and teams. While speech recognition has been around since the 1960s, advanced AI in the form of machine learning, natural language processing, and even computer vision has expanded the capabilities of today's transcription tools. Before, such tools could only record all the words that were being said. Today, algorithms can analyze, paraphrase, and summarize entire transcripts.

Companies are looking for new ways to help today's professionals. According to a Cisco survey, one in four respondents spend half their day in meetings.[155] People need help collaborating so they can focus on actual work. The same Cisco survey showed that 95 percent of workers believe AI can improve work tasks. Artificial intelligence improves employee satisfaction in the form of digital assistants, relationship intelligence, and computer vision.

In China, schools use computer vision and facial recognition software to inform teachers in real time about their students' engagement level. Based on behavior (e.g., how intent students are when looking at the whiteboard or how many times they glance elsewhere when the teacher isn't looking), the software can suggest which students are engaged and which are distracted. The software can recommend to the teacher which student to call on to keep them engaged.

This type of software can be repurposed for other scenarios such as public speaking, team meetings, and corporate training. For such scenarios, the goal isn't to call out bored and distracted people in the audience. Instead, it's to alert speakers that they need to quicken the pace, move to another topic, tell a joke, or perform other techniques that make them better collaborators. A dependable assistant that slightly nudges a speaker when she's beginning to lose the room can be a game changer.

Over the next decade, AI will transform from a simple command and control bot to a strategic team member. Armed with data and analytics, AI will suggest ways to grow revenue, where employees are needed, and onboard new hires. AI will free up humans to unleash our creativity, engage in high-level tasks, and build stronger teams.

A growing number of companies use virtual reality to train employees to become better speakers. In a world where we spend most of our communication typing or texting, we're not as used to communicating face to face, let alone a whole group of people. VR speaking companies like Ovation recognize that public speaking is key to professional development, but there are limited opportunities to practice in front of an audience. VR experiences simulate meetings, conferences, and other public speaking events where various challenges can occur. Our brains perceive a VR audience the same way as real people. That presence helps anyone from people with a fear of public speaking to seasoned professionals harness their craft and communicate their ideas.

Working Together Worlds Apart

Many information workers can now do their work in less-populated areas with fast Internet access if they are concerned about the virus or the environment. When people ask, "When are you going back to the office?" I tell them that many people will be working remotely for the foreseeable future. Why do I need to live near a physical office if I'm interacting virtually? I should be able to live anywhere as long as I am available when needed.

Companies are recognizing that keeping people in an office wasn't so much about culture as it was about control. However, companies can still foster productivity and communication with tools that people are already using and maintain desired outcomes while people work from home. Instead of people not talking to each other face to face in the office, employees are now just doing that from home.

Many workers have slowly become "stateless." This won't just snap back to the way it was. This means someone could move from their corporate hometown in New Jersey to Hawaii and most people wouldn't know it since they only see a virtual background during Zoom meetings. "Stateless" could also refer to a worker who moved from America to Slovenia and didn't tell anyone. We recently heard of a worker who managed a secret move to Slovenia (true story) and it went undetected for quite some time. Besides the time zone change and the complexities of taxes with foreign workers, there seems to be little reason for others not to follow suit should they want to live in a more exotic location. For instance, if you'd like to live and work in Iceland, Capetown, Lagos, or Montevideo, why not? We're confident our work performance would remain the same, if not be improved. How about you?

Employers need to find new ways to connect people remotely as slews of online meetings become tiresome or exhausting. Technology is a great way to provide presence, assistance, and provide a digital community. However, companies need to help employees step away from work when it's just a cell phone app or headset away. Remember, the better the employee experience, the better outcome for the company and customer. We have the tools to seamlessly transition to remote and digitally nomadic lives. Let's use it responsibly to create the best outcome for everyone.

Apps to Collaborate and Communicate

To date, virtual reality has yet to find its "killer app." Meanwhile, investors, startups, and even big companies like Google are still developing that perfect combination of price point, value, and accessibility to drive trial and adoption. While some of these apps may phase out over time, the important thing is that virtual and augmented reality provide the most natural place for people to collaborate and communicate outside from being together in person physically.

Holo, It's Nice to Meet You

There's an evolving ecosystem and vocabulary around telepresence.[156] Among other tech giants, Microsoft is exploring the space with R&D around a working concept called "holoportation."[157] Using a combination of mixed reality (a form of AR that anchors virtual objects to the real world) and 3D capture technology, holoportation allows people to see, hear, shake hands, and interact with other people from remote locations as if they're physically present in the same room.

So if you're having a meeting and somebody wants to ask another participant a question, you can give them a way to do so without disrupting the process. Using holoportation, anyone can quietly approach other virtual participants and converse in an unobtrusive spot without distracting other meeting attendees. Once 5G becomes the norm, this capability can be established anywhere, not just in remote high-tech centers with $100,000 worth of Cisco gear installed. In the near future, such collaborative technologies will allow us to talk with each other as holograms or as high-fidelity volumetric videos that may be projected into a conference room. Moreover, said technologies greatly improve the quality and efficiency of remote work, which will likely move organizations to reduce office maintenance and travel costs.

For organizations, 5G can help preserve employee uptime, even amid economically and socially disruptive events such as an extended lockdown from a pandemic. On the other hand, workers gain the ability to be present from anywhere and contribute to value generation regardless of their location. When creating and maintaining tight connections becomes effortless, people can focus more on important things instead of fussing about trivial concerns such as whether network bandwidth is enough for a video conference. Propelled by enabling technologies, creative minds can explore more design possibilities of systems that make life awesome for everyone. Innovation teams can tackle pressing real-world problems and formulate effective solutions. Architects can collaborate remotely to study shadow studies of skyscrapers and ensure that neighborhoods get to have enough sunshine and scenic views of the skyline. Urban planners can test how new, sustainable materials can withstand structural stress or build the blueprints for aesthetically pleasing, sturdier, and nature-centric communities of tomorrow.

These activities aren't science fiction. They're already happening in many parts of the world. In many cases, you can access these experiences as easily as playing a video game with a VR headset.

During 2020's WSJ Tech Live, Cathy participated in a small interactive group discussion with the avatars of WSJ technology columnists Joanna Stern and Christopher Mims, and Spatial's CEO, Anand Agarawala. During this live in-person virtual reality meeting attendees got a peek into what it is like to "return to the office" in VR.

Reinventing Meetings

Virtual meeting rooms are the most common virtual reality apps on the market. There are over a dozen to choose from at any given time. The same thing could be said for teleconference tools. There are so many VR conferencing and collaboration apps because they make the most sense. People feel a real physical presence in virtual reality. There are fewer distractions (theoretically), and teams can perform rituals like daily standups or present a prototype as they would in real life.

Flow Immersive is one such type of tool. Designed for collaborative meetings with shared visualizations and diagrams in augmented reality, it's designed for Magic Leap devices but also works on the web.[158] Using this program, users can collaborate around data visualizations in 3D from anywhere in the world. A variety of apps are designed for multiple devices, and companies seek to galvanize market-share.

In Spatial, "Your room is your monitor, your hands are the mouse."[159] Spatial is betting its success by being available on several devices like Oculus, Hololens, Magic Leap, and the Web.[160] Creating an avatar with Spatial is as easy as taking a selfie. In fact, a photo-realistic avatar is made in seconds with your smartphone. This then enables you to be in a meeting as a holographic presence. People search for an item and then can visualize it in their workspace. With their hand, they can write notes, draw, or present diagrams to others. Spatial has created a virtual piano that enables musicians to create music with all ten fingers by merely touching the air. By being available on so many devices, Spatial makes collaboration and communication accessible to almost everyone in a way that will turn into a natural means of virtual presence.

True Virtual Collaboration

In 2016, Microsoft developed a product line of customer relationship management and enterprise resource planning applications that it calls Dynamics 365. According to Microsoft, "Dynamics 365 is a set of intelligent business applications that helps you run your entire business and deliver greater results through predictive, AI-driven insights."[161] Recently, Microsoft integrated this suite of products into their mixed reality smart glasses, HoloLens.

Now, and in the near future, instructors in various industries will be able to develop corporate training programs that harness augmented reality training. In construction, an operator could virtually tour dozens of digital worksites before he even steps foot onto an actual one. In health care, a doctor could practice operating on hundreds of digital patients, via her smart glasses, long before she operates on a physical one.

Microsoft Dynamics 365 also comes with Remote Assist technology. Remote Assist allows to "collaborate more efficiently by working together from different locations with Dynamics 365 Remote Assist on HoloLens, Android, or iOS devices."[162] This will enable employees to share their real-time view with experts in remote locations to get the help they need and to stay hands-free.

Businesses will save money as employees "walk the site without being on location." Companies will reduce costs with remote inspections as users combine video, screenshots, and annotations for more seamless workflows on current devices.[163] Microsoft's spatial collaboration tools aren't likely to go away since they've invested heavily in the Hololens. Project Service Automation and Power Virtual Agents are just some of the tools on Microsoft's product roadmap.[164] These use predictive insights from AI and IoT to enhance training, efficiency, and business performance and relationships.

On the Horizon: VR for the Masses

Facebook Horizon is a social VR app developed by Facebook for Facebook VR devices. It's meant for virtual social gatherings and communication. Facebook defines virtual, social presence as "authentic and lifelike collaboration between people and colleagues in a virtual setting."[165] It's where anyone can manipulate objects, use their hands, and have a sense of touch. Avatars display the same expressions as their human counterparts. Spatial presence includes audio, where the closer you move to a noise, the louder it gets. Horizon provides marketing opportunities in three areas: representation, play, and world-building.

A brand's representation is different in virtual reality. Representation means becoming part of a customer's world and presenting a brand or business as a real being people can interact with in a natural way. Facebook demonstrates this in Horizon by deploying staff who will act as guides or hosts in public spaces. Facebook is changing the customer service experience from submitting a request, to being able to virtually walk up and talk to a Facebook employee.

One of the features of Horizon is games like mini golf, escape rooms, paint balloon, or a battlefield where people wield virtual swords. Facebook wants Horizon to be collaborative and interactive. This gives brands a chance to get in on the action. Who wouldn't want to see Wendy's versus Burger King in a virtual paint ball fight? The winning team gets a free burger.

Marketing in virtual reality takes a different approach in this new evolving space. In Facebook Horizon, people can build their own worlds. Marketing teams can use this feature by building their own worlds for customers to explore. Hide Easter eggs (hidden items placed in movies or games) such as discount codes or free items for explorers to find. Companies could harness the excitement that Ready Player One brought to VR by building a world where one lucky winner could rule it for a day.

Creating a world for a brand within Horizon or branded virtual objects that Horizon users can reuse in their own designs are one way to take part in this new, social world. Instead of shooting a commercial in real life, brands can shoot one in Horizon, using real, virtual customers as extras. They can then live stream the commercial (and making of it) to Facebook and shared across platforms.

Collaboration, gameplay, and world-building are all tools with which marketers need to familiarize themselves. Social presence in spatial computing will only get more advanced, especially as companies, like Facebook, ease the barrier to entry. Marketers would do well to experiment now, so they can be part of the virtual worlds like Horizon.

The convergence of both the physical and virtual worlds creates new opportunities for friends, families, and even colleagues to connect. The future of connection will push the boundaries of today's technology, one virtual world at a time. It's crucial to be aware of social VR apps, especially Facebook, as this is the next frontier for marketing. Facebook hasn't officially stated that ads will be on Horizon, but it does require Oculus users (Facebook's headset) to link their Facebook accounts. Plus, Facebook will likely integrate their own cryptocurrency, Facebook Libra, into Horizon. We expect Facebook to monetize Horizon at some point, so companies should be fluent in the app and ad types for virtual reality. Virtual reality creates presence so designing marketing campaigns in VR is closer to the physical world than online. People will remember the way your brand's experience made them feel. It's about striking a balance between letting the customer explore and modeling the experience for them.

The giant experiment of the COVID-19 pandemic has shown companies and their employees that remote, virtual collaboration is possible. What's more, that collaboration is no longer limited to slow or low-fidelity interactions. Companies and workers that leverage these new technologies have an opportunity to benefit from more diverse resources and faster iteration towards more successful outcomes.

Opportunities to Augment Collaboration

- *AI is helping presenters monitor and react to their audiences' attention.*

- *XR is helping people come together and in shared workspaces, with more tools for understanding, and in larger groups.*

- *XR is enabling many remote experiences, saving on travel expenses and logistics: remote sales consultations, design collaborations, training, and inspections.*

- *5G can help people collaborate in more places, at faster speeds and with more detail.*

CHAPTER ELEVEN

Customer Service:
Automating Satisfaction

AI has been at the center of customer service for quite some time. Customers don't mind talking to a bot because they're able to get their questions answered instantly. Artificial intelligence gets better at answering a range of customer questions the more it's used. Customer service AI has evolved from simple queries and responses to conversational bots, so much so that people can't tell if they're talking to a human or not.

Companies are developing digital humans so that when you visit a webpage, you might think you're interacting with a human with unique facial gestures and idiosyncratic reactions, but it's just a program. AI is what underpins that. Granted, our current stage of AI relies more upon branching narratives or conditional logic, but more autonomous artificial intelligence is being developed. Cash bail in California is being handled now with AI algorithms because so many cases get backlogged. In Chicago, AI is being used to handle eviction cases. A person can scan an eviction notice on their phone, and an AI attorney helps them with their options.

AI reduces risk to humans and parent companies in a number of ways. Insurance companies employ AI embedded drones to take pictures of roofs, instead of sending humans to dangerous heights. AI can compare millions of damaged roof claims for insurance companies and assess the damage as to whether it's due to normal wear and tear or a weather-related event. Drivers can use AI-powered insurance companies, like Lemonade, on their smartphone to submit photos of damage from a car accident, and AI will address the claim.[166] Sometimes claims are resolved in mere minutes. Anytime there are tens of thousands of claims that need to be processed, AI helps companies scale in creative ways.

Artificial intelligence is eating around the edges of various industries, slowly infiltrating in multiple sectors. AI is insinuating itself into customer service. People become more reliant on technology for assistance as it becomes easier to talk to a customer service bot than wait to talk on the phone with a human.

XR for Customer Service

Augmented reality is also being used in technical and customer support. Suppose a customer was having trouble operating an appliance such as a washing machine. They could point their smartphone camera at the appliance, turn on the video function, and a customer support representative would be able to see and interact with the video stream. The customer service rep could use a virtual chalkboard feature, similar to what commentators use during football games, to circle a particular button to show the customer how to use the machine properly. Then, the representative could tell the person to pivot the camera to the back of the machine and unhook a pipe or change a setting. The customer can play back their service call on a 3D model of the appliance so that they can refer back to the instructions later. As the customers move their phone, orbiting around the object, the directions can update. This adds another layer of intelligence to the customer's phone, saves the customer from waiting on hold on the phone for forty minutes, and saves the company from sending out a technician or responding to various emails. Augmented reality empowers customer service reps to be as helpful as possible, breaking through the screen or phone to interact with their customers as if they were in the same room.

As AI, XR and 5G advance, customer expectations are increasing for quick, effective, and personal resolutions to their issues. Companies must keep pace—and have an opportunity to innovate and succeed as well.

Opportunities to Augment the Customer Service Industry

• *Predictive AI is being used to anticipate customer needs, making suggestions before a customer realizes she has a need.*

• *AI chatbots are being used to handle simple customer interactions and to train CSRs.*

• *XR is being used to support DIY and collaborative customer troubleshooting.*

• *5G is enabling higher-fidelity customer support experiences.*

CHAPTER TWELVE

Agriculture: Yield of Dreams

Many think that America's farms are the last place you'd look for high tech. Consolidation and worker shortages have led to a dramatic change in this millennia-old industry. Farmers turned to self-driving tractors, vertical farms, and artificial intelligence drones in 21st century farming.

What does an augmented workforce look like for your industry?

Nate Fender, co-founder and COO of Ario Technologies:

"The technology just is. That's when you know you've got it right. Tangibly, this looks like personalized information delivery to anyone and everyone on the frontline in an industrial environment.... A truly augmented workforce will see the marriage of spatial context with disparate data in an elegant way. Information might be visual, it might be aural, but without a doubt, it will build confidence in the worker's ability to achieve their desired outcome. Industrial environments can be high-pressure, so it's our

obligation to keep frontline workers at the forefront of our minds as we iterate on technologies to help solve the toughest challenges they face. "[167]

Augmented Tractors Get a 5G Upgrade

"5G will change the nature of jobs in farming and agriculture substantially," but it will take some time for carriers to make networks available in rural areas.[168] That isn't stopping the agricultural industry from transforming into high tech. Through automation, electrification, and artificial intelligence, tractors like John Deere show how agriculture can be more sustainable and productive. Electric tractors lower emissions and use less fuel. Embedded systems in the seed sprayer track where seeds land, including the soil type to estimate crop yield.

Drones Replace Crop Dusters

A field may look like an endless view of plants but to drones powered with AI, each plant is unique. "With their bird's eye view and advanced sensors, a drone can gather data on 500 to 1,000 acres in less than a day."[169] Artificial intelligence in drones tell the difference between cultivated crops and weeds, reducing the amount of pesticides[170]. Drone-powered aerial photography uses computer vision to diagnose disease or identify plant stress. At harvest time, robotic harvesting systems use computer vision to identify and pick fruit. Not only are robots cheap to build and faster than humans, but they can also recognize the ripeness of the plant it's harvesting.[171] Drones, powered by AI and eventually 5G, increase the yield of high quality crops that's less costly to farmers.

Vertical Farming in the Big City

Agriculture is transforming more than the type of equipment farmers use. The nature of what constitutes a "farm" has evolved. Vertical farms are set up in urban areas. Scientists grow plants instead of farmers. Vertical farms use AI to empower robots that analyze, feed, and treat food using 250 times less water and space.[172] Plant scientists monitor data from the specific light recipe of each plant, the amount of fertilizer, and humidity required. Vertical farming allows for plants to be in season year-round. Since they're grown in urban environments, the food can be delivered to people faster and more cheaply than produce shipped across the country.

Technology upgrades in agriculture are more than cool new toys. Robot harvesters cost less and collect data on each piece of produce they pick. Drones and seed sprayers collect data on each seed sown and plant grown, turning farmers into data scientists. Vertical farms allow plant scientists to test changes quickly and customers are more sure of what they're getting because plants are analyzed closely. Robots, AI, drones, and eventually 5G allow farmers and food scientists to experiment, iterate faster, and create better food outcomes for the planet— people and the earth included.

Opportunities to Augment the Agriculture Industry

• *AI simulations and drone-powered computer vision applications are helping growers plan and diagnose their crops.*

• *XR training is helping workers build better products more safely.*

• *AR sales and remote support tools for Ag equipment can help far away customers feel valued.*

• *5G coverage will be sparse in rural areas for years to come.*

CHAPTER THIRTEEN

Architecture / AEC: Computer-Aided Craftsmanship

Think of architecture and technology and you may imagine 360° photo tours of vacation spots or faster hotel wi-fi. In fact, the architecture industry is much more advanced, revolutionizing the way things are built. Blueprints are now often digitized into augmented reality visuals. Construction crews see 3D engineering diagrams updated in real time on 5G networks. Tradespeople have more freedom to design and complete projects.

What does an augmented workforce look like for your industry?

James Ashley, 3D Development Lead at VIMaec:

"As with any large coordinated effort, from making a movie to building a skyscraper, there are always too many people onsite who don't need to be there unless something extraordinary happens. A clearer vision of these projects and more effective use of communication

technology will streamline and clarify project plans, allowing more people to do useful work instead of waiting around a construction site just in case."[173]

Virtual Architectural Design Reviews

In one project in Australia, bricklayers used mixed reality headsets instead of 2D drawings to view design instructions. The bricklayers did more complex designs with mixed reality because they could see the whole project laid out before them.[174] They didn't have to switch between looking at a paper blueprint and the site for installation. The headsets allowed the bricklayers to work in larger, more complex teams because everyone could see the same design and interpret it in the same way.

Construction crews use mixed to reality to see the mechanical, engineering, and plumbing systems while they're working, avoiding costly mistakes and dangerous errors. For example, local and remote project members see, real time, the measurements of an area, detecting clashes before pipes are installed. Mixed reality tracks issues on the physical site and in the shared model at the same time.[175]

In 2018, Cathy and John worked with Oldcastle, a multi-billion dollar building materials company, to use AR via a mobile phone app for one of their most popular concrete products, Sakrete. The augmented reality based Sakrete App uses spatial computing to help workers measure different jobs more efficiently. The app recommends the correct Sakrete product and quantity and directs users to their closest retail location for purchasing. Cathy and John worked closely with their marketing team to bring the AR app to life, which launched at World of Concrete 2019.

The release of the company's first foray into AR, aligned with Sakrete's commitment to leverage innovative technology to serve its customers. By viewing and capturing the project site through a smartphone's camera lens, contractors were instantly provided the appropriate product selection and quantity, eliminating the need for manual calculations. The Sakrete app was the first of its kind in the concrete industry to use augmented reality to calculate bags of concrete needed for a project. It helps contractors save time and money for their customers.

5G Real-Time Updates for Construction Crews

Crews that work with digital designs over a network may have problems on a construction site. Construction managers can quantify the dollar figure on waiting for a 3D model or document to download for their contractors on site. 5G networks will erase data bottlenecks. Instead of starting a download and going for a cup of coffee while crews wait for the data, construction managers and contractors can access documents or models instantly and see real-time updates from designers.[176]

Smart Vending Machines for Construction

Smart vending machines aren't a new concept for manufacturing plants or construction crews. But they got better over time and will continue to do so with 5G. Smart tool cribs from Cribmaster and others offer vending machines that hold tools and equipment for workers. They only release tools based on the employee's role or position. It also keeps track of tools and who last checked them out. Smart vending machines automatically reorder supplies, like ear protection, when stock runs low. Smart vending machines free staff to focus on their work instead of keeping track of inventory.[177]

Those in the AEC industry are using these technologies on their projects to save money, time, and even lives. They help crews work together smarter and faster by creating smart systems and reducing mistakes. What's most exciting about XR in construction is that it empowers tradespeople to develop their own templates, locate services, or schedule construction.[178]

Opportunities to Augment the Architecture Industry

• *Architects use AI to produce parametric designs for greater efficiency and strength.*

• *AI enables firms to test ideas quickly to reduce stress, weathering, daylight, etc.*

• *This rapid iteration allows for more collaboration, higher confidence, and better outcomes.*

• *Models and data can be shared across departments.*

• *AEC vendors can be more collaborative with end-customers.*

• *Customers can be more sure of what they're getting.*

• *Digital twins help the actual, built structures to stay closer with plans.*

CHAPTER FOURTEEN

Automotive and Aerospace: Moving Technology

No matter how small technology makes our world, we still have to move, and when we do, we depend on machines to get us there quickly and safely. Manufacturers of vehicles, from supersonic jets to the humble bicycle, face challenges to improve, to innovate, and to design machines that are attractive, cost-effective, and safe.

Many people believe that robots are taking over, and it's easy to see why. Today, modern factories are full of precision machines assembling products in total coordination, often running with the lights off in the plant, with little human intervention. But this isn't the whole story.

Humans haven't left the industry—they've just moved. They've moved to roles that require our unique creative and analytical talents—things machines have yet to master. The following examples explain how the workforce in the automotive and aerospace industries are using XR, 5G, and IoT to deliver more value than ever before.

Designing Products with
Artificial Intelligence

Autodesk combines human creativity with machine learning to accelerate the product development process in a new form of artificial intelligence called generative design.[179] Generative design uses the power of the cloud to explore multiple solutions to a product from additive manufacturing, subtractive, and casting. Generative design is an example of empowering a design team because they can focus on the design options that work instead of doing the work of figuring out the best variation. Lightning Motorcycles used the process of running machine learning to redesign the swing arm for one of their motorcycles. The AI found five different designs for the swing arm that met the quantitative goals of being structurally sound and lightweight while also maintaining the "ride feel." The generativity designed swing arms matched the original design in four use cases and even outperformed the original by 55 percent in the fifth load case.[180]

Artificial intelligence, like the kind used in Generative Design, shows engineers a new way to conceptualize manufacturing processes. "We haven't seen a whole lot of shapes like those of generative design and a manufacturing process like casting overlap. That is largely just cultural; it is not a technical reason," said Andreas Bastian, Senior Research Scientist at Autodesk. Engineers may be used to using additive manufacturing, but machine learning and artificial intelligence shows them that other methods of manufacturing, like casting, have flexibility in design too.

Companies also use artificial intelligence to sort through large amounts of data to maintenance equipment as well. Delta uses AI and machine learning in their aircraft maintenance strategy.[181] AI and ML are capable of generating specific work orders for maintenance technicians, instead of a person having to sort through and analyze large amounts of data into an action item. AI maintenance alerts can trigger on parts, tools, and routing of the aircraft. AI learns over time based on the more data it gets so it can go from analyzing the past to predicting the future. AI can help technicians catch problems before they happen.

Virtual Reality Design

Automotive designers are rethinking vehicle development. Designers and engineers at automotive companies like Toyota, BMW, and even the aerospace company Gulfstream, use virtual reality to build the latest vehicles because traditional engineering tools are too outdated for their design process.

At Toyota, virtual reality is now a better tool for designers and engineers to test vehicle ergonomics than using real people in a virtual environment. Ergonomics are more than the comfort of the seat. Toyota tested a car's visual field by adding cyclists and pedestrians in the VR simulation. Mikiya Matsumoto, the general manager of the Prototype Division, Digital Engineering Department at Toyota said, "The test enabled us to improve visibility and we were able to complete it very quickly at a low cost compared to conventional methods."[182]

BMW used a similar mixed reality simulation to design the BMW iX.[183] They collaborated with Epic Games to use their Unreal Engine to quickly develop and visualize interior concepts, vehicle functions, and visual experiences. Designers and engineers were able to work through these design matters more quickly and since they take place in the beginning of the process, the entire timeline to build the car was shortened. Tools like virtual reality give designers and engineers a "new level of flexibility." They're able to experience real life road conditions while sitting inside an actual car.

Design comes in more forms than in the factory. Air Canada uses virtual reality to showcase its business class seats. They partnered with Neural Digital to recreate their seats for trade shows around the world. "We created not only the seat, but also the whole passenger experience to show how great the service is," said Sergio Irigoyen, Head of VR at Neutral Digital.[184] The VR experience included almost everything someone might interact with on an airplane like adjusting fans, turning the reading light on and off, and eating a meal. The VR Air Canada experienced reduced costs of transporting an airplane seat to trade shows. It also made the experience come to life so that potential customers could envision themselves in a luxury airplane, not just in a seat at a convention center.

5G Virtual Collaboration

BMW is upgrading their plants for digital innovation with 5G networks. BMW Brilliance Automotive (BBA) is BMW's joint venture in China. BBA is testing 5G by rolling it out across all their plants. They're testing procedures and developing new innovations with 5G to improve industrial productivity.[185] 5G's high data rate, rapid response time, and security of the network make augmented and virtual reality, "wide-scale networking of machines, and the use of autonomous logistics fleets" possible use cases.

Training Ground Crews

The military is one of the first to embrace immersive reality. There are endless training scenarios and "bogies" in XR. At the Columbus Air Force Base in Mississippi, pilots train faster using virtual reality.[186] Virtual reality cultivates the skills pilots need such as situational awareness, risk management, and decision making. Plus, it augments the training student pilots go through so they can pause a flight mid-air to look around at the equipment. They can then continue the flight without becoming overwhelmed. Virtual reality doesn't replace actual flying (yet) but there's no doubt it helps develop better pilots faster.

Delta Airlines has thousands of flights per day. They need to keep those flights moving in a safe, quick, and efficient manner. They do that with people, specifically workers in ramp operations. Delta turned to virtual reality to implement procedural training. They used a simulated Delta jet and arrival gate to educate employees on walk-around inspections without having to "clear up ramp space, tie up valuable airplane operating time, or risk employee safety."[187] The VR training used auditory cues and visual instruction to guide trainees through the experience. The benefit of VR simulated training like Delta's is that you don't have to spend time in a classroom. You can put inexperienced or new employees right on the virtual job. Virtual reality is learning by doing, those memories and actions stick with workers once they start the job in real life.

In the summer of 2017, Cathy advised UPS as a VR expert prior to the launch of their VR driver training program. UPS wanted to train student delivery drivers to spot and identify road hazards using VR headsets. The virtual reality software vividly simulated the experience of driving on city streets while teaching a more memorable classroom lesson. The VR training modules replaced the touchscreen devices UPS Integrad facilities used to teach lessons on road hazards.

AR Support

The automotive industry is always looking for ways to drive customer experience beyond the automobile itself. Companies use augmented reality to help customers learn how to operate their vehicle. It can be daunting for the driver to learn how to navigate their new car since hundreds of functions are now "hidden" on a large screen. That's why Mercedes-Benz turned to an augmented reality app to replace traditional owner's manuals.[188] Mercedes-Benz is known for sleek, high tech cars. An AR app continues that experience. Plus, it reduces the amount of paper Mercedes normally uses to print manuals. Customers can ask the app's virtual assistant questions like, "How do I charge my phone?" The app is a first step toward augmented customer experience. A customer may not know how to turn on their air conditioning since it's in a particular menu on the touchscreen display. Drivers can also use their phone as a two-way manual while technicians teach them how to operate the car utilizing AR.

As our world becomes ever more connected, technologies like AR, AI, and 5G are helping us make the most of the time we spend moving. Together or on their own, they can be used to make it cheaper, faster, and safer, too.

Benefits of Augmenting the Automotive and Aerospace Industry

• *Virtual simulations with AI increase safety and confidence.*

• *Test changes occur quickly and cheaply with XR collaboration and AI simulations.*

• *5G offers faster and frequent collaboration (no travel or lost sleep, less downtime).*

• *With XR marketing, customers are more sure of customization choices and the end product.*

• *With 5G, collaboration and sales support can happen in remotely or in the field.*

• *All sessions can be record and analyzed, and shared across departments.*

CHAPTER FIFTEEN

Defense: Fighting Back with Technology

Using the latest technologies in the defense industry doesn't sound surprising. The defense industry created the ARPANET, the precursor to the Internet. You may think that the defense industry is focused on technology-enhanced soldiers, but the latest technology is used for more than that. Augmented reality allows expert technicians to assist maintenance operators in the field. They reduce the downtime of aircraft and keep everyone happy.

Artificial Intelligence for Defense

The United States of America operates the most powerful military in the world, and the country's Department of Defense has pursued innovation through Artificial Intelligence. A 2018 summary of the DoD's AI strategy makes it clear: "We will harness the potential of AI to transform all functions of the Department positively, thereby supporting and protecting U.S. servicemembers, safeguarding U.S. citizens, defending allies and partners, and improving the affordability, effectiveness, and speed of our operations."[189] They aim to improve the effectiveness of surveillance systems, of weapons, and of the soldiers and commanders that wield them. As we learned a few chapters ago, AI applications can be used to help with recruiting, answering questions and determining fitness. They can be used with training to tailor material to the trainee's learning style. Surveillance imaging can leverage AI to detect anomalies or patterns. Just as they help us organize the photos on our phone, they can be used to spot threats. Combat systems can handle more data and offer greater decision support. When seconds count, real-time findings from AI systems can help the military make better decisions.

Remote Assist Technology

Not everything in defense has to do with soldiers and weapons. The defense industry has a large manufacturing base and is largely made up of maintaining "assets." Assets are equipment or vehicles like aircraft, humvees, and military ambulances. Militaries and defense contractors have service techs around the world, ready to repair and maintain assets. In the past, when field techs faced a problem they didn't know how to fix they had to take multiple photos and email them to a subject matter expert (SME) at the corporate office. Augmented Reality took that process, which took days, and turned it into a matter of hours. Librestream is one company transforming the defense industry with their augmented reality system, Onsight.[190] SMEs instantly connect with the field tech, the specific problem, and through any AR enabled device, walk the tech through the steps to fix it. Recorded sessions provide a database for other field techs to experience the walkthrough before calling an SME.

Augmented Reality for Military Dogs

The term "super soldiers" has become part of pop culture. However, the U.S. Army incorporated augmented reality in a unique way. The Army noticed a communication problem between soldiers and their military dog counterparts. Handlers use hand signals to communicate with their dogs but that requires them to be close to their dogs which is a safety issue. Dogs usually scout dangerous areas where explosives or hazardous material may be. Dogs are issued specially fit augmented reality headsets that display visual cues. The handlers see everything the dog does and command it through the headsets.[191]

AI is critical for military defense organizations, and it represents a new kind of arms race for governments and their militaries around the globe. It is with a great deal of hope that we suggest these technologies can be used to make us all safer, whether it's to plan, to secure, to defend, or to disarm.

Opportunities to Augment the Defense Industry

• *Leaders are using AI for decision support, gaming out possibilities.*

• *AI simulations offer more iterative experimentation toward better, safer outcomes.*

• *Soldiers and support teams are using XR for just-in-time training on equipment and missions.*

• *Buyers can be sure of what they're getting with XR tours, configurators, and previews.*

CHAPTER SIXTEEN

Education:
Learning Without Limits

Humanity has never had access to so much information, so many opportunities to educate oneself, and yet the amount of information required to succeed in Western society has never been higher. There is more pressure on aspiring career employees than ever. They need to be skillful, strategic, resourceful, and versatile, and to communicate professionally.

Today, only a few people operate independently. We collaborate over video conferences. We rate and comment on each other's work. We edit live documents. In fact, during the 2020 global pandemic, this high-speed cooperation has been on display across industries, as each of us work and adapt with the changing times. And yet, most of us will need retraining to remain employable as how things get done continues to change. Luckily emerging technologies are an accelerant to the people who have the determination to create a better life for themselves.

AI for Education

While education is all about developing your own intelligence, AI can offer a lot of help. Today, educators and students alike use narrow, focused AI applications to analyze learning styles, test performance, and customize recommendations for additional materials and exercises. Soon, AI will be used to adjust instruction and supporting materials for the learner's age, their language, ability level, their device, and even the time they have available to learn. In places where the ratio of students to teachers keeps growing, AI can help support everyone's progress—customizing experiences, and perhaps even reacting to them as they learn, reading their pace, expression, and progress toward more effective learning.

Digital avatars are a new asset to training and education. These digital beings, brought to life by AI and virtual reality bring personalization to education. "In the VR training industry, AI-powered avatars offer some really exciting possibilities, especially for soft skills training," said Tom Symonds, co-founder and CEO at Immerse. "A trainee could be in a virtual training environment speaking to an avatar that could respond in real-time to provide relevant feedback and guidance, performed by AI," Symonds said.[192]

"This is really powerful as it allows you to create immersive VR training scenarios that aren't prescribed," said Justin Parry, co-founder and COO at Immerse, "they're context and AI-driven rather than pre-formulated and content-driven."[193] Instead of students interacting with traditional video-game-like non-playable characters, they have their own personal tutor in the form of a digital avatar. The avatar is powered by AI that learns from a specific syllable or curriculum.

XR for Education

At the intersection of XR and education, there are inspiring examples where enthralled students marvel at the solar system, chemical compositions, dinosaurs, historical events, and physics demonstrations. This is happening across subject matter and domain. NASA is teaching its astronauts in VR simulations and even mobile phone retailers like Sprint are using augmented reality to teach salespeople about the products they offer. Companies across the spectrum are pushing to create curriculum including technology companies, startups, studios, publishers, and individual educators and students alike.

Data is the new oil in the digital economy. That data can be used for every student or trainee to fine tune their education through personalization. What makes the technologies in the six pillars so powerful is when they work together. AI, combined with virtual reality will supercharge educational standards and learning delivery.

5G for Education

As devices and software continue to become part of the education equation, the demands on the network have increased dramatically: more connections, needing more greater capacity and quicker speeds. Technologies like XR and cloud computing are bandwidth-hungry. They need instantaneous response times to work effectively. After many years of marketing, 5G coverage is rolling out across the US and around the world—offering better connectivity to students, educators, and schools.

Greater access to high speed Internet enables an explosion of devices and content to coexist—permitting new educational experiences to help expand our minds. 5G connects teachers and students virtually, with high fidelity—allowing for multi-user participation and collaboration. Now that the capability is finally arriving, there is immense opportunity (and pressure) for content and standards to make the most of this potential. Given the education sector's generally slow pace, startups and larger companies alike have a helpful role to play.

Building the Future

There are lots of opportunities to help create educational content with these technologies too. Nearly all XR is built using "game engine" software. Companies like Epic Games offer over dozens of online tutorials and classes in their Unreal Engine. People can learn how to use the software towards a new career in animation or interactive development. Democratizing learning, removing the six-figure cost of a college degree, and offering cutting-edge training to equip the next generation means that more people can find success and contribute to society regardless of their background.

Dr. Joachim Scholz (Brock University) sees great potential for universities to capitalize on XR technologies, especially in the age of COVID-19. He argues:

> *Universities around the world must ask themselves: 'How can we welcome a new cohort of students and build a school spirit without coming together during first-week events, on-campus classes, and varsity games?' Both AR and VR can help. While VR can (temporarily) replace and supplement campus tours, AR can create community even though students are dispersed around the country and the world.*[194]

Instead of looking at barriers to implementing this, Dr. Scholz points out that the class of 2025 is already a power-user of social AR, thanks to their love for Snapchat and Instagram. He encourages universities to create AR lenses to help incoming students identify themselves with their school and celebrate their acceptance into their dream programs.

Ready Learner One is an innovative learning solutions provider. Founded by a team of instructional designers with a passion for innovation in learning and training practices, Ready Learner One challenges the status quo when identifying and implementing learning and training in both the education and corporate spaces. The CEO, Dr. Micah Shippee, sees enormous potential between AI and voice recognition. He remarked:

> *AI learns through the data we generate in our real-time efforts. One form of AI is voice recognition. Voice*

recognition has come very far. With early voice recognition software, we had to 'teach' the computer how we spoke so that it could translate our sounds into text. Today, voice recognition software is incredibly powerful and able to live-type the words that we speak at an unbelievable speed. Voice recognition is a perfect example of how AI can positively impact our classrooms.[195]

Dr. Shippee shared that he has experienced this impact in his own life. He has always wanted to write and blog more but lacked the time. Voice typing has been the solution. "I simply open a Google Doc, voice type, and start my brain dump. The result? More writing, more blogging. So, why not use this same strategy with students?" Without these technologies, he believes that typing will continue to be a barrier to creativity and output. He explains:

In two decades of teaching middle school, I have seen so many students stare at the keyboard as anxiety built up over where the keys were on the keyboard and how to type properly. Their focus was on re-coding their thoughts onto the buttons. Think about how much of a student's well-thought-out message was lost as they try to type at the same speed as they think or speak. It begs the question: How many beautiful stories have been lost to the ages because of the demands of keyboard devices that were solely designed to help mechanical arms avoid entanglement? Voice recognition is the next generation of crafting powerful messages which will resound as truly authentic narratives [and will] assist writing rather than drive it.

Roger Spitz is the founder of Techistential, a global foresight strategy and futures thinking practice based in San Francisco. He shared with us how emerging technologies will revolutionize education, turning it from rote learning to personalized entertainment while still effectively educating the student. "What is clear is that the current education system, which is reliant on knowledge and where, in its current teaching format, [it] is difficult for many subjects to be genuinely engaging for the majority of students (history, geography, arts, even sciences), there is an important role for XR, and 5G will enable this." When these technologies (AR, VR, and Spatial Computing) are combined, enabled by 5G, and carefully designed, they can, as Spitz told us:

[A]llow for the student's imagination to explore different subjects in a democratized way (i.e., anywhere, anytime, anyone), while personalizing the learning. These technologies can help engage students to embark on a journey of discovery in an immersive and gamified way, whereby education becomes personalized entertainment, without it being a less effective learning journey.[196]

What does an augmented workforce look like for your industry?

Roger Spitz, founder and CEO of Techistential:

"The 'Augmented Workforce' for a leadership team or entrepreneur is where algorithms and machines have an increasing role in the 'value chain.' From optimization (e.g., automation) to augmentation (e.g., predictive analytics, pattern recognition, opportunity detection, risk reduction, etc.) to creativity support (e.g., scientific research, drug discovery, or drafting legal contracts and negotiation support). It is these AI-enabled predictive insights (at scale and for unstructured data), which can support and augment human strategic decision-making."[197]

Along these same lines, Dr. Micah Shippee, CEO at Ready Learner One, states:

> *Technology is a disruptor. Like the printing press changing who could read and the pencil changing how we were taught to write, the Internet has changed how we can more easily access knowledge. Emergent tools will continue to change us. At first, we integrate these tools by adding them to what we do, but eventually, if we find real meaning-making through the tools, we will adopt them. In education, we do not talk about learning with a pencil since we have adopted the pencil into how we learn. It is just what we do (we have adopted it). However, we still talk about learning with a computing device as an integrated tool plugged into our educational system. We know when a technology-based disruption is complete when we stop referring to the technology as an independent aspect of what we do and understand it as just what we do.*[198]

AI, XR, 5G break down barriers to learning. Technology makes learning more natural because they remove the need to first learn how to type or use a computer to gain access to information. We're not saying that students don't need to learn how to use computers. The whole point of this book is the augmented worker. Workers and students become augmented when technology learns how to work with them, instead of workers having to learn how to use the technology. Artificial intelligence and extended reality will become an extension of students, expanding their abilities to learn and retain information. Students will be able to express their ideas in many new ways as they learn to leverage the six technology pillars from Chapter Three.

Opportunities to Augment the Education Industry

• *Educational platforms can use AI to adapt course materials and instruction based on student interaction data.*

• *Educators are using AR and VR to help students visualize places, objects, events, or concepts that are hard to grasp.*

• *5G in the classroom and in the field is helping bring rich experiences and lightning-fast Internet to students.*

CHAPTER SEVENTEEN

Media and Entertainment: The Show Must Go On— Everywhere

Without a doubt, the media and entertainment industries have had an enormous influence on technology since the advent of television. Increasingly, they seem to be locked in a self-sustaining cycle of technology enabling new and better content and experiences, which requires better technology as it improves. This is not going away anytime soon. People in the media and entertainment industries should think about how to apply AI, XR, and 5G to the future of entertainment. Let's talk about how these technologies are used in the media today.

AI for Media

We rely increasingly on recommendations with ever increasing libraries of things to experience. Anyone who's ever used YouTube or Netflix knows this. Whether you're starting from the home page or finishing a final season, you face that choice of "what's next?" Today, technologies not dissimilar from AI are making those recommendations based on what you've liked and other people like you have liked as well. In 2018 it was revealed that Netflix markets the same shows differently inside their app, changing show graphics based on users' tastes[199]. In the near future, this will extend to the influence of those shows' content as well.

With the advent of more lifelike computer-generated characters, "deepfake" videos and lifelike synthetic voices, AI will customize narratives that can be "painted with data" to reflect what we're more likely to enjoy. Whether it's through your viewing history or facial expression, AI will tailor the stories you are told. Of course, our entertainment won't be limited to linear media experiences like videos. AI enables us to speak to virtual characters through lifelike facial animation and voice assistant AI. Do you like *Game of Thrones*? You can spend an hour with a synthetic "Mother of Dragons." Do you prefer sports? Ask famous athletes and coaches for their opinion on this weekend's big game. Wherever there is repetitive labor, there is an opportunity for automation and AI.

XR for Media

The "family room" first appeared in the 1945 book, *Tomorrow's House,* by George Nelson and Henry Wright.[200] It was a place where Americans began to make room in their homes for their radio and eventual TV. For nearly eighty years, our connection to entertainment has been inching closer to a convergence between the cinema and a comfy couch. However, since the advent of mobile video and gaming, that trend has reversed, and quickly.

Today, we can have impactful media experiences everywhere, including immersive technologies like augmented and virtual reality. In popular titles like *Star Wars: Vader Immortal*, consumers use VR to live within the stories they love. The AR touchstone title *Pokémon GO!* has shown how augmented reality brings stories into the real world.

Creators use virtual reality production techniques to plan and "shoot" film in VR, as if they were on set with the animals. Examples include the live action remake of *The Lion King* and *Jungle Book*.[201] Most of season one of

Disney's popular streaming show *Star Wars: The Mandalorian* was scouted in VR on virtual sets shown on massive LED walls.[202]

Filmmakers adapt these techniques for TV shows and even commercials. Broadcasters use a type of augmented reality to make more elaborate shots of talent on live-action stages. Sets, props, performances and more are captured in volumetric scans, allowing them to be played back from any angle. Increasingly, these technologies are being used beyond pre-production planning and into the productions themselves. Traditionalists expected that digital cameras would never replace traditional film, but many of them now shoot exclusively digital. Of course, this isn't only for creating or consuming pre-produced content, it's affecting live events too.

From 2016 to 2017, Cathy served as Chief Communications Officer for a cinematic VR studio, Future Lighthouse. During her time there, she worked with a very progressive and futuristic team that brought to life the first branded campaign ever to be nominated for a Tribeca X Awards, BeefeaterXO. The studio was ahead of its time. It brought three of the Venice Film Festival's VR Selections to life: Melita, Snatch (in partnership with Sony Pictures), and Campfire Creepers (in partnership with Oculus and WME and featuring Robert Englund who played Freddy Krueger in the Friday the 13th horror franchise movies). Despite the amazing creative output from the studio, Future Lighthouse closed its doors in 2018. Its closure was very similar to many VR startups that have had a hard time raising funds. They were ahead of their time and many of the team has gone on to work with major VR studios and companies.

Flash forward to the summer of 2020. John and Cathy attended an award-winning play—a virtual performance of "Finding Pandora X"[203] as part of The Venice Film Festival[204]. Later that year, we joined revelers at electronic music legend Jean-Michel Jarre's New Year's Eve concert in a virtually reconstructed Notre Dame.[205] These experiences are truly participatory, allowing the audience to travel to imagined worlds and shape events as they unfold. Customers will be expecting much more from live events, with examples like this, especially as an alternate option as the world meets face to face again.

5G for Media

With more to see and do, we'll need more bandwidth to experience it all. 5G already allows us to take higher-impact experiences to new places, whether it's playing a multiplayer game from the highway, or watching a 4K movie while we're camping in the wilderness. On the workforce side, there are many uses for 5G. Remote production crews can communicate more easily, previewing their work with stakeholders. Distributed teams can collaborate, guiding or shaping the work remotely. Complex computations like visual effects are done in the cloud, and in real time, allowing for companies to operate anywhere and perhaps even rent the expensive computer equipment required for this work. News crews capture ever more data for networks, allowing producers more options to tell the story and viewers more ways to experience it, even in augmented reality where it's blended over the real world.

"Virtual production" for film and TV has exploded in popularity due to social distancing and quarantine protocols. Using LED screens to represent a natural background, actors can perform in front of a screen. The television audience can't tell whether the actors are on location or using a digital medium. A great example of this was Disney's *Star Wars* series *The Mandalorian,* which used LED backgrounds to great effect. These stages are often located in places without high-speed Internet, so 5G can save the day and enable virtual production.

The world of entertainment is changing. What constitutes as entertainment today will be different tomorrow. Who would have thought ten years ago that people could make a living live-streaming video games, or play those games over the cloud on any device? Or that Tik Tok clips of just a few seconds would capture whole audiences and make people famous? The lines defining what is entertainment, gaming, music, and reality itself are merging. In the next ten years, games, subscriptions services, and other forms of digital entertainment will increasingly merge. The blurring of what constitutes a game, TV show, or movie will create new and exciting ways for people to express themselves.

Shopping as Entertainment

Instagram is a service where people spend hours watching their friend's "stories" or scrolling through IGTV. But it's becoming more interactive. Users of the app try on virtual makeup from companies like L'Oreal. If they like the look, they can buy the makeup directly from Instagram. Shopping and entertainment are converging even more in what Andreessen Horowitz General Partner Connie Chan calls "Shopatainment." In a formula she describes Entertainment + Commerce + Content = Shopatainment, it's an evolved form of infomercials. Shopatainment creates a bond with the buyer and seller through storytelling. [206]

Machines Build Video Games

Video game creators will need more than artistic skills. They'll work with AI coworkers. Machine learning and AI can take the burden off game studios' hardest workers. Rovio, the globally renowned mobile game and content studio behind the Angry Birds franchise, uses machine learning to lighten the load of their game designers. Machine learning helps designers produce fun content faster with less manual work. Phil Harrison, Vice President and GM at Google said of what the gaming industry might look like in 2030, "we will see some adjacent technologies like machine learning, AI, and natural language fuel game design tremendously. Imagine being able to walk into a world and have a truly believable conversation with a character, where it feels like you're talking to a real human being—they remember you, they remember your backstory." [207]

The End of the Game Console?

5G has also enhanced the gaming world edge computing and 4k streaming. Now, a person's web browser can be a "dumb terminal" while all the real computing power takes place nearby in the cloud. 5G is delivering this experience, as you can see with Microsoft's Xbox Cloud and competitor Google's Stadia. Edge computing via 5G is great for entertainment but is being used for other applications such as simulation and training. If a device isn't powerful enough to deliver a 4K experience, wherever a high-impact and high-accessibility experience is needed, edge computing can make it happen.

eSports out from Behind the Screen

Augmented and virtual reality change what it means to game (or interact with any of our devices). Remote controls, video game controllers—even virtual reality controllers will be a thing of the past. Hand tracking brings people's whole bodies into the game. Even flipping through subscriptions or streams on the TV will be a swipe of the hand.

People will "play games in our real-world spaces and with our bodies, instead of using controllers that are already starting to feel so obtuse."[208] That means a new reality for eSports. Mixed reality brings players out from behind the screens. Players will compete in the real world, battling a digital game overlaid on top of it.

The Sound of Music

Augmented reality does more than enhance our sight. It changes the way we interact with the world through audio queues. This has a big impact for the music industry. "Augmented reality has the potential to be the next format for music, and the reason for that potential [is because] it puts fans at the heart of experiences, and it's authentic,"[209] Facebook is now testing new AR filters on its new Portal TV hardware that could potentially "allow folks to 'have a

lip sync battle with Grandma, where [you] look like a rap bad-
ass and she looks like a rocker.'"[210]
There could come a day when performance halls service not
only physical audiences and performers, but virtual ones as
well. Alex Coulombe is the Creative Director of Agile Lens, a
NYC XR studio that is crafting the future of live events. He told
us:

> For live performance, it's all about finding new ways to
> bring an audience together. We've worked on projects that
> developed new methods to do this in everything from
> prototyping an app that live streams 360 stereo video
> (Samsung Event360), to fully virtualized live
> performances that can be viewed by anyone in the world
> (Alive in Plasticland, Loveseat, Jettison).[211]

How will 5G and XR work together to change the
entertainment industry? Coulombe continues:

> Spatial computing and 5G will be crucial tools in the
> performance toolbox of the future. Imagine one audience
> on-site for a live show, but a substantially larger,
> secondary audience from around the world streaming an
> experience to their phones or headsets. Performers may or
> may not be on-site— some could be streamed in as
> holograms from other live locations. Maybe some of those
> holograms are not live (in any sense), but rather,
> sanctioned, posthumous replays of lauded performances
> presented in new contexts. In some cases, we'll see the
> absence of a physical theater as the actors become fully
> remote and virtual.
>
> Beyond the live show, what if a once-in-a-lifetime event is
> captured volumetrically or with motion data? Rights and
> unions-permitting, that opens up entirely new revenue

streams by releasing content after the sets have been broken down and performers have moved on to other work. Examples of this can already be seen with The Key, Chained, and The Grinning Man.[212]

"When given a choice between a 2D video of a fantastic production and a spatial VR replay that lets him navigate the stage and get up close to world-class musicians and actors, Coulombe said, "I would choose the VR replay every time!" Never before have there been more ways to inform and entertain us. Never before have the tools been this sophisticated. Companies that leverage AI, XR, and 5G in this industry will have greater efficiency, agility, and speed. They'll also have the ability to build long-standing and deep relationships with their audiences.

Opportunities to Augment the Media and Entertainment Industry

• *Creators are leveraging AI for set design, animation, and visual effects to build more diverse and realistic scenes.*

• *Films and TV shows are using VR to direct animated sequences in real time.*

• *Augmented reality is being used in television and live shows to incorporate live actors with CGI environments.*

• *5G will allow film crews to leverage real-time visual effects and compositing to live. shoots, bringing remote stakeholders to the set and reducing the need for post-production.*

• *Augmented and virtual reality experiences are being used to market and extend valuable intellectual property, creating devoted fans and keeping them close.*

CHAPTER EIGHTEEN

Financial Services: Technology with Interest

For most people, the height of financial services technology is online banking. Depositing a check directly with your bank's app is great, but this industry is much more technically robust than it seems. Firms invest in virtual reality to view data, artificial intelligence to analyze accounts, and smart assistants to help customers.

Re-envisioning Data

In 2014, Fidelity Labs, a part of Fidelity Investments, created a virtual world called "StockCity" where stock portfolios turned into a virtual 3D city. There, investors immersed themselves in the data.[213] Buildings represented different stocks and funds. The height and type of the building represented how well the stock was performing—all without displaying any numbers. It takes skill to create 3D visualization of data the people can interpret in a meaningful way, but when done correctly it outperforms 2D graphs and charts.

Salesforce uses Oculus Rift to create an immersive 3D environment for analyzing data.[214] The tool helps financial services workers map out various data-driven scenarios for wealth management. In one example, people enter what looks like the inside of a tornado of colors, each one representing data. The speed and width of the rings represents different information for an analyst—all without words or numbers.

Artificial Intelligence-Powered Agents

Fidelity Labs introduced a virtual financial agent, called Cora. She operates with voice commands to answer questions and presents relevant information to the client.[215] Capital One created Eno, a natural-language SMS text-based assistant that "generates insights and anticipates customer needs through over 12 proactive capabilities, such as alerting customers about suspected fraud or price hikes in subscription services."[216] Eno also works as a browser extension to generate virtual card numbers. Customers generate secure card numbers while keeping their actual card numbers safe from potential fraud.

Younger generations prefer mobile banking, and 5G will make financial services like machine learning-powered chatbots, direct-to-consumer banking and no-fee trading more secure and powerful.[217] Through virtual and augmented reality, everyday people can understand their portfolios because data is represented in a way that naturally makes sense to them. They can make decisions based on 3D representations of numbers and accounts.[218]

Opportunities to Augment the Financial Industry

• *AI chatbots can answer investor questions.*

• *AI simulations can help investors with decision support.*

• *Banks are building VR branches.*

• *Cryptocurrency empowers buyers to have true ownership of digital media.*

• *XR to help investors visualize complex data and concepts.*

CHAPTER NINETEEN

Healthcare: Prescribed Progress

Healthcare is an industry where everyone benefits from technological augmentation. From doctors and nurses to patients, the six technological pillars increase doctor's capabilities and patient's health. Technology in healthcare allows doctors to practice digital surgeries with real patient data. Patients don't have to travel to get the care they need through advanced telehealth. These are a few of the ways healthcare is transforming for the benefit of all.

Virtual Patients: Real Needs

Even though this book deals largely in a business context, it's important to remember that we're all consumers and patients too. John shared an experience of his own:

I went to the eye doctor recently, and it was tough to try on various glasses because I was wearing a mask. Each time I wanted to try a pair, I had to take off the mask and hold my breath. I actually didn't end up buying the glasses at the store because it was such a cumbersome experience (taking off my mask, holding my breath, and wearing glasses that the eye doctor just sprayed with sanitizer). A much safer alternative is virtual try-ons. So, I sat in front of my computer, and I used my phone for virtual trials and was more comfortably able to see which lenses looked best on my face.

AR already helps consumers who are looking for virtual solutions they can use in the comfort of their homes. It saves travel time, gas costs, alleviates health concerns, and can be done at the customer's convenience, outside of normal business hours. Virtual trials are used for all manner of products including jewelry, watches, shoes, dresses, and more. People use virtual dressing rooms and the companies that leverage AR for these purposes see an increase in customer satisfaction and sales.

AI Diagnostics: Testing Will Never Be the Same

Artificial intelligence is transforming diagnostics. Cancer and skin diseases are most successfully treated when caught early. Scientists tested an artificial intelligence neural network (Deep Ensemble for Recognition of Melanoma [DERM]) to evaluate images of potential skin cancer gauging whether or not a patient is at risk for melanoma.[219] The AI was tested on 7,102 dermoscopic images. The study concluded that DERM achieved an "area under the curve" better than primary care physicians, which makes it a potential diagnostic support tool in primary care. In other areas of healthcare, radiologists use AI to determine which parts of the lung deserve closer attention so that they can focus on scanning rather than poring over detailed images. Doctors want to do their best to help patients and patients want to live healthy lives. AI can assist with both.

Virtual Reality Surgery

Stanford medicine combines imaging from MRIs, CTs, and angiograms to create 3D models that physicians and patients can manipulate in VR.[220] Surgeons prepare for surgeries better than ever because they have 3D models based on real patient data. It puts the patients at ease too because they can understand what's going on in their bodies by looking at a 3D version of themselves instead of trying to understand an MRI scan.

VR in Pain Management

Clinical trials use virtual reality to manage acute and chronic pain in patients. VR has shown to be a promising pain management tool for patients with a variety of chronic conditions like phantom limb pain and fibromyalgia. A publication on virtual reality as a clinical tool for pain management found that, "VR trials demonstrate a potential to redefine the approach to treating acute and chronic pain in the clinical setting."[221]

Another study, researchers discovered that there may be more to virtual reality than a pain distraction tool. In studies that combined VR with other treatment modalities, such as biofeedback mechanisms and cognitive behavioral therapy, neurophysiologic changes related to conditioning and exposure therapies were produced. In essence, "VR may have the ability to help reduce opioid use and misuse among chronic pain patients."[222]

Volumetric Video Training

Volumetric video is deployed in training because it engages the brain differently than 2D media. "We've learned how brain engaged employees are when trained by content captured volumetrically," explains Tim Zenk of Avatar Dimension, Microsoft's newest licensed volumetric studio in Washington D.C., based on Microsoft Mixed Reality Capture Studios technology. "It results in more knowledgeable employees because they learn from every angle. Enterprises have reported that using this technology sees enormous efficiency gains while increasing the quality of training skills learned."[223]

The University of British Columbia captured live medical training in volumetric video using two 4k cameras. Volumetric video allowed the university to distribute the same types of cases across the province where it was traditionally difficult to connect patients with students. The project captured patient-physician interactions, 3D models of organs, and physical test results for the students to diagnose the patient.[224]

Whether it's for training, education, regular checkups, preventative medicine, diagnostics, surgical procedures or ongoing care, the applications for AI, XR and 5G for healthcare are everywhere.

Opportunities to Augment the Healthcare Industry

• *AI simulations can test new treatments.*

• *AI computer vision and machine learning can identify disease or atypicality from photos and medical imaging (X-Ray, MRI, etc.).*

• *XR training can be used for physicians and support staff.*

• *XR marketing and sales support can be used for new medicines, tools, and devices.*

• *5G enables better communication and more data in mobile telehealth apps.*

CHAPTER TWENTY

Hospitality:
Augmenting Arrivals

As this book is being written, many are "hunkered down" around the world due to the global COVID-19 pandemic. Most hotels, once brimming with guests streaming in and out of their doors, sit empty—their once-busy staff, now idle, are furloughed, or worse. Moments of economic uncertainty might not seem like the time to think of augmenting the workforce, but there could not be a better opportunity to imagine the future. Let's take a look at how technologies like AI, XR, and 5G influence the hotel industry.

AI for Hospitality

Kai-Fu Lee, Chairman and CEO of Sinovation Ventures and respected author of *AI Superpowers* talks about how "[h]umans need and want more time to interact with each other. I think AI coming about and replacing routine jobs is pushing us to do what we should be doing anyway: the creation of more humanistic service jobs."[225] Despite all the tech we've surrounded ourselves with, we are humans after all. Having more time to focus on each other—to make our moments away from home more compassionate and more comfortable—would surely be better. Artificial intelligence frees up time for us to do just that.

Anywhere there is scale and a lot of data, there is great opportunity for automation. Whether it's your first time staying in a hotel, or if you're a road warrior, your travels create a lot of data: where you travel, how long you stay, your activities while you're there—all the choices you make. Just as e-commerce retailers are ever sharpening their keen knowledge of our preferences, modern day innkeepers use data to make things just right for us. AI is used to forecast hotel capacity, plan ahead of demands for amenities, and suggest that guests repeat successful choices.

AI is used to predict maintenance needs, anticipating and proactively repairing or improving all the high traffic spots in a guest experience that experience inevitable wear and tear. Housekeeping leverages machine learning with computer vision. They can scan empty rooms to detect departures from a hotel room's "brand standard." The AI reports and recommends that the pillows are out of place, that the soap needs to be refilled, or that lost TV remote is located. Like an invisible robotic butler, AI is guiding more of our steps and prepare the way before us as we travel from home.

XR for Hospitality

Perhaps we spent more time enjoying our destinations in those storied days when business travel was glamorous, before the invasion of 24/7 connectivity and the ever-present distraction of mobile devices. Now however, we spend more time looking at our devices, running between meetings, or back to our hotel rooms and room service, with many messages to read and write before we sleep. Let's look at some of the ways XR technology can improve this situation.

As we just learned, AI helps hotel housekeeping and maintenance staff anticipate issues or put things back in place. AI and XR when used together, train service teams by simulating guest needs and how to accommodate difficult requests. At Portico.AI, hotel staff are trained using a conversational AI based on a database of guest interactions.[226] Using VR or even a laptop, trainees and staff seeking continued education, immerse themselves in various customer touch points to improve their skills. Employers use software and approaches like this to effectively train staff and measure their competencies.

The value doesn't stop with the staff, however. Increasingly, people look to VR for entertainment, escape from moments on the road. Wireless VR devices like Facebook's Oculus Quest VR headset, give road-weary travelers a mental escape hatch from the mind-numbing view of another standard double room. Armed with virtual reality, travelers train for their next meeting, blow off steam, or reconnect with dislocated friends and family. They can sample nearby client entertainment spots and find nearby excursions or other activities they'd like to try.

Mobile augmented reality directs travelers in unfamiliar places, showing them turn by turn directions at arms' length or propped up on the rental car's dashboard. For hospitality staff, and guests alike, technology is smoothing over pain points and creating new opportunities for all involved.

5G for Hospitality

Since the days of dial-up, hotel connectivity has been a challenge for travelers. Even with the advent of wi-fi, the dense concrete structures found in many hotel buildings have proved a frustrating challenge for guests and proprietors alike. Even with the dawn of mobile 5G, penetrating hotel structures will remain difficult, and guest connectivity is likely to remain a frustration. Guests will bring more devices with them, and with a year's experience working on their home network largely without disruptions, they'll have increasing expectations for good reception, and hotels may feel pressure to make wi-fi faster or free. Hotels that want to lean into the marketing promise of 5G may need to invest more deeply in their wi-fi infrastructure to keep guests happy.

As business and leisure travel returns again, guests will rely on these technologies even more to research, to book, to travel and enjoy their lives. The companies and teams that serve them can still prepare, and those that do will succeed.

Opportunities to Augment the Hospitality Industry

• *AI service chatbots can communicate with guests to handle many requests.*

• *Computer vision can show guest-room staff which areas need attention.*

• *AI can predict maintenance needs.*

• *XR training with simulated guests can help staff learn to handle complicated situations.*

• *XR can improve hotel marketing.*

• *5G can provide guests with better connectivity and entertainment.*

CHAPTER TWENTY-ONE

Real Estate: Automating the Business of Locations

Long ago, home buyers pored over newspaper classified ads or drove around looking for "For Sale" signs. Commercial real estate agents depended heavily on networks to know which properties were available. Today's industry would be nearly unrecognizable, by comparison. Buyers are armed with real-time data and analytics to aid their search. Sellers use a variety of digital media to entice buyers, and agents rely on technology more than ever to connect them and sign deals. Things are changing again, and the AI, XR, and 5G play a large role.

AI in Real Estate

Buyers and agents face an overwhelming amount of data to consider when it comes to real estate. AI helps make recommendations on areas to watch, which properties are ripe or have high potential, and how likely certain offers will be successful. In residential real estate, services like Houzen help property owners find worthy renters or buyers quickly, filtering on success rates, local expertise, and accreditations.[227] Redfin offers agents a specialized AI-driven search tool they claim produces listings 400 percent more likely to be clicked than a homebuyer's own saved search.

In commercial real estate, AI helps companies make better use of their existing spaces with apps like IBM's TRIRIGA, which collects data from wi-fi usage to understand where workers go and stay.[228] Real estate investors use AI platforms like Geophy's Neighborhoods to analyze multiple data sources, including traffic, demographics, amenities, and safety, to predict price movements and identify solid opportunities.[229]

XR in Real Estate

If the first rule of thumb in real estate is "location, location, location," the second rule must be that "a picture is worth a thousand words." Over the last twenty years, as more data is available to buyers, seeing properties has become more of a chore. With so many to see, agents and buyers spend days shuttling around areas to get a closer look. This has been more difficult for relocations or remote investors, and especially challenging for properties currently in planning or under construction.

Increasingly, buyers and investors alike are relying on immersive technologies like augmented reality and VR to select their next property. Virtual Tour platforms like Matterport offer a professional solution for capturing and displaying interactive panoramic 360-degree imagery.[230] Home improvement-focused 3D scanning startups like Hover, help sellers make measurements from mobile photos, take measurements, and explore presale improvements.[231]

Agents use augmented reality to showcase staging suggestions with furniture and even light remodeling (paint, lighting, etc.). Commercial real estate companies are marketing with augmented reality too. They use headsets, tablets or phones to show off properties and amenities from any angle, even if they have yet to break ground. Using XR in real estate reduces risks and saves time for both sides of the bargaining table, and creating these experiences is getting easier all the time.

5G in Real Estate

Property managers will benefit from 5G in a number of ways. The faster connectivity of 5G means faster response times to residents' requests, in turn marking happy customers. Property managers can pass on savings from using 5G to residents. And property data can be made more secure because 5G allows for decentralization of data, which means completing transactions more securely. [232]

Increasingly, agents and brokers need to understand the power of these tools and how to wield them. Customers are quick to share information with each other, and if the agents aren't leveraging AI's ability to stay on top of the data, they may find themselves left behind. According to Paul Daugherty, Chief Technology and Innovation Officer, at Accenture, "The playing field is poised to become a lot more competitive, and businesses that don't deploy AI and data to help them innovate in everything they do will be at a disadvantage."[233] The same applies to other experiential technologies including XR.

Opportunities to Augment the Real Estate Industry

• *Investors are using AI to determine where and when to purchase properties.*

• *AI can predict maintenance needs for rental properties.*

• *AI can help tenants navigate complicated eviction processes.*

• *XR marketing is supporting property sales and leasing.*

• *5G and IoT allow for remote owners to keep track of building utilities and maintenance needs.*

• *5G provides greater connectivity for some apartment dwellers for remote work and entertainment.*

CHAPTER TWENTY-TWO

Sports: Changing the Game

Sports games, players, and the stadium experience are no longer stuck to the TV screen. Sports teams and coaches are turning to immersive technology to enhance the game. Sports teams realize the potential for virtual and augmented reality experiences. They've been building on the technology for the past few years. As 5G connectivity is installed in more places, the reality of immersive sports can come true.

Smart Stadiums Use AI and Wi-Fi 6

Investment in the digital transformation of sports stadiums grows as the industry is expected to reach $614 billion by 2022.[234] The SoFi Stadium in Los Angeles partnered with Cisco to use Wi-Fi 6, the next generation wireless standard. More than 2,500 Wi-Fi 6 access points will deliver faster speeds for immersive-experience applications, more bandwidth, and higher reliability, all while being less taxing on a device's battery.[235] It will be the largest deployment of Wi-Fi 6 in a sports stadium. Jason Gannon, managing director, SoFi Stadium and Hollywood Park, envisions the stadium not just for hosting sports, but as a "dynamic media platform"

Watching sports in person is fun but waiting in line to park or use the restroom is not. Artificial intelligence installed in networked cameras in parking lots guide visitors directly to free slots and prevent traffic jams when everyone leaves after the game.[236] Similarly, AI enables "smart" cameras that detect queues building up for the bathrooms. When fans use a smartphone app, the AI can guide them to less busy restrooms and concession stands. Increasingly, these sports arenas and stadiums are using security platforms that leverage facial recognition and IMEI tracking to identify known security threats and/or suspicious behavior, alert and direct authorities, and route law-abiding fans away from danger during an emergency.

Watch Sports in VR and AR

This book was written during the 2020 pandemic which shifted everyone to work remotely and stay away from crowded events like sports games. Luckily, sports leagues turned to immersive technology like virtual and augmented reality to continue the experience for fans around the world. Many of these immersive experiences are dependent on 5G connectivity. Companies like Verizon are stepping up to develop concepts for new formats with 5G, VR, and augmented reality (AR) to bring immersive content to sports.[237]

Virtual reality brings sports back to the home and younger audiences who don't watch TV. Virtual reality puts fans back in the stadium, racetrack, or boxing arena. In VR, fans aren't stuck to the "nosebleed" section. They can jump around from camera angle to camera angle, watch the game in silence, or join others from around the world.[238] Anyone who can find ways to improve VR sports streaming or simplify viewing and replays is in a good spot to reap the huge potential the VR has in sports.

Augmented Reality Benefits Fans and Coaches

Augmented reality benefits fans by immersing them in the sports experience. Think about how it can benefit referees and judges. Tennis competitions use an AR technology called Hawk-Eye that recreates ball trajectory.[239] This assists judges in the decisions of the play (plus, fans can use it to test their skills in comparison with world-class players). Coaches use augmented reality, with the help of a 3D camera, to record their players. Coaches use AR to highlight technique and possible corrections. One example is DribbleUp, a Soccer app that comes with a special ball that records the player's moves and compares them to a virtual trainer and gives feedback. AR apps like this means players can practice without constant supervision and coaches could possibly take on more clients.

Volumetric video is a way to bring real sports players into fans' living rooms. "Volcap video solves a significant content challenge for our clients, especially in Sports and Entertainment, who want to feature their athletes and actors in augmented reality," said Jason Yim, CEO and Executive Creative Director of Trigger. "In the past, we were limited to integrating 2D video or 2D green screen footage into the AR experience. Or we could 3D model the talent from scratch, which was prohibitive from a time, budget, and likeness approval standpoint, but now with volumetric video, fans can place the talent in their own environment in a three-dimensionally accurate and more importantly, magical way."[240]

For millennia, sports have captured people's attention, emotions, and money. Once the domain of only the most athletic and brave, sports today cover a range of skilled activities. These exponential technologies are taking those opportunities even further, giving some fans greater access to the sports they love, and allowing others to participate more than ever before. At the same time, the players, agents, coaches, and venue operators have greater tools at their disposal to make decisions, to attract and retain fans, and to deepen their connections with them.

Opportunities to Augment the Sports Industry

• *AI is helping to shorten waits for fans on shared resources like parking lots and restrooms.*

• *5G is improving connectivity on premises for fans to enhance their experience.*

• *Volumetric video capture is allowing athletes and coaches to study essential sports movements for improvement.*

• *XR experiences are enabling fans to have an immersive or augmented experience when they can't attend in person.*

CHAPTER TWENTY-THREE

Transportation: Moving from A to B(eyond)

No matter how productive so many information workers have become while working from home, at some point everyone will have to move again, and as they do, they'll find exponential technologies driving things forward. Here's how:

AI for Transportation

Nearly everyone on the planet is accustomed to travel by car. Traffic, construction detours, distracted drivers, weather delays, accidents. It's a modern day bane of existence. Artificial Intelligence is starting to help. With every passing year, more semi-autonomous vehicles are on the road, sensing lanes and other vehicles, steering and braking, "drafting" behind others to save fuel, and communicating with infrastructure to improve traffic flow and increase safety.

In the near future, we'll see more fleet vehicles go from merely GPS-enabled to autonomous driving as delivery workers work between stops. Autonomous public transport will allow drivers to pay more attention to passengers. Intersections and signals will be able to adjust for higher flow during peak traffic periods, and route first responders more effectively in emergencies.

Together, smart vehicles and smart infrastructure will lead to smart cities with people and goods moving efficiently even as things get more crowded. Of course, we'll still need to know how to drive, for a while anyway, but increasingly we'll have more time for work and other things. In one respect, workers will have to worry less about piloting their vehicles, which may make some uneasy initially. However, our transportation workers will be freed up to learn new skills and take on new responsibilities around passenger service, maintenance, and other activities. We should expect the world to run more smoothly as well, as AI applications and systems predict maintenance needs on vehicles, lights, roads, bridges, and railways.

XR for Transportation

Our time on the move will be liberated once our attention is safely off the road and connected with 5G mobile broadband. At street level, augmented reality is improving our view of the world with more information around the vehicle and on the world around us. Passengers can use VR to access dramatic new environments for both work and play. While en route, service workers can use augmented reality to support customer interactions, find the next packages on the pallet, determine where to find important parts and tools, as well as how to use them.

Virtual reality allows for deep and real-time collaboration with others. Today, we can join a conference call even if we're late to the meeting. With VR, it will be closer to actually being there. VR is also providing additional on the job training through simulated tasks and scenarios. Once the nearly exclusive domain of startups, now organizations as large as the New York City subway, are getting in on this. Underground, this modern city is still utilizing rails and switches that are nearly eighty years old, and training materials haven't kept pace with technology or modern teaching techniques. Their transit agency used 3D scanning to bring these old parts into the 21st century. Now, instead of waiting for their chance to train on ancient cast-iron equipment, they can practice key maintenance tasks from any browser, phone, or XR headset. In the sky, air travelers are more likely to have a VR headset to wait out long gate delays and gain some quasi-privacy on long-haul flights. Gulfstream is letting customers configure aircraft cabins in VR. Air Canada's passengers are wooed with sophisticated VR marketing.[241] Flight attendants are using mobile augmented reality to locate, serve, and protect the safety of hundreds of passengers across more than a dozen types of aircraft. Delta's ground crews are using VR to learn how to inspect and service jets_between flights.[242] As a complex industry with lots of pain points, exponential technologies are helping air travel in myriad ways.

5G for Transportation

Our connected lives won't stop when we leave home or work behind. 5G technology reaches us in transit as well, speeding connections on the sidewalk, in the air and between. As with the advent of 2G, 3G, and 4G LTE, we'll all do more on the go—needing less and less from an office and a desk.

Opportunities to Augment the Transportation Industry

• *Autonomous vehicles are using AI to move people safely and efficiently.*

• *Cities are using AI to help with traffic flow.*

• *AI is helping cities predict when and where repairs are needed.*

• *Cities are using XR to train maintenance workers on essential repairs to rails, roads, and vehicles.*

• *5G is allowing for commuters and travelers to make more of their time in transit, for work and play.*

• *5G is empowering better communication between vehicles and infrastructure.*

Part III:
Look Ahead, or
Be Left Behind

CHAPTER TWENTY-FOUR

Should We *Brace* or *Race* for Change?

No matter which industry you're in, we hope the preceding chapters help you roll out this technology throughout your business. Each step works together to upgrade the entire business process, including product and people. You don't have to give VR to everyone at once or install 5G networks in every plant, but you should think about the big picture: How 5G enables higher-quality virtual and augmented reality solutions. How artificial intelligence applications can run more securely on 5G and can be visualized with AR or VR. Starting a digital transformation may seem daunting. Done well, digital transformation saves money, builds agility into the business, and makes room for more experimentation for overall better outcomes.

Business transformation through these keystone technologies is inevitable because the benefits are beyond compelling. To ignore new tech at this point is to yield advantage, revenue, and market share to competitors. Amid the availability of game-changing technologies, running your business as before means limiting your growth potential and lowering the bar for what your company can otherwise achieve. Anything that dramatically lifts business efficiency, accelerates processes, cuts expenses, scales output, enhances product quality, or improves decision-making, deserves your immediate attention.

The future of culture and humanity has never been more influenced by digital technology than today. Generation Z and younger feel that technology (from the Internet to social media) is part of who they are. They see their digital lives as an extension of themselves. This mode of thinking opens up a whole new avenue for creative problem-solving, marketing and product storytelling, entertainment, health care, and customer relationships. Brands can use technology to make their products and sales pitches more personable, targeted, and individualized than ever before with digital human representatives and personalized AI customizations.

Ethical Questions

These exponential technologies open a Pandora's box of ethical and moral questions. Since companies will have access to even more data in the augmented world than they do today, debates about privacy concerns will heat up. The difference is, this data won't just be behavioral. It will also be biological. Brands won't just be able to track eye movements and clicks on a screen. They'll be able to track and analyze brain waves, thought processes, and the intent of their customers. It's one thing for Amazon to know their customer's browsing history for the purpose of pitching products. It's another thing for Amazon to be able to analyze a customer's mood, glances, emotions, and attractions. Will that data be held safely on an Amazon server or sold to interested parties?

According to technology writer Barry Levine, even now, "ad agencies and researchers are regularly analyzing eye-tracking to measure attention, facial expressions to determine positive or negative emotions, galvanic skin response to gauge the intensity of emotions, brainwaves for determining patterns of mental responses, and other signals to get the kind of unfiltered info that conscious answers can't supply."[243] This data and these insights are intensely personal, therefore customers will not want them shared.

Privacy and security must be a top factor for companies moving to augmented work, or else they will quickly lose their customer's trust and loyalty.

The digital divide will take shape in a new split between privacy savvy, digitally minimal consumers, and those who want the convenience that technology provides. Unfortunately, many data privacy-focused customers feel trapped: "Across countries as diverse as the United States, Canada, the UK, China, and India, between 80% and 90% of consumers said they wished there were more companies they could trust with their data."[244] Even though consumers don't trust the businesses they use, they don't switch because the next company is just as likely to be untrustworthy with their data. Faced with no other options, one in ten consumers are dropping out, meaning that they expect their overall usage and engagement with technology to decrease.

Fortunately for marketers, nine in ten are sticking around. "Most consumers (76%) recognize that sharing data with companies is a 'necessary evil,' and recognize the benefits in doing so."[245] Convenience of personalized recommendations, AI assistants, to even something as simple as saving passwords and credit card numbers, are some of the conveniences that lead people to hand over their data, even if they don't trust the company to handle it.

Spatial computing and AI companies are already poised to disrupt markets. Cybersecurity is one more area where they have a chance to win over customers that are dropping out or giving up. Customers who don't trust companies to handle their data responsibly will share the bare minimum, which will make using the data to bring a better customer experience that much more difficult.

In the past decade, social media went from being cool (like a private club), with never-before-seen features on the Internet, into an ominous oligopoly called "Big Tech." Social media sites' algorithms feed their users exasperating and scoff-inducing content, creating vast cultural divides. The more outrage they can generate, the more they can keep their audience engaged.

People who use these services are concerned about data breaches, a lack of data transparency, and political biases within the corporations, which inevitably filter out important content. Social media apps like Instagram went from being a place to "show one's window to the world" to an ad-driven site where the default thought is that nothing is real. If monetization continues to remove social connections and authenticity, then various VR, AR, and XR versions of this form of communication will fail.

Businesses making the leap to the future have the chance to reset the ethical standards that the past decade has discarded. Companies like the AI Foundation are already taking steps to ensure that AI technology is developed ethically. Their mission is to "to responsibly move the world forward by giving each of us our own AI that shares our personal values and goals." The AI Foundation leaders see their company as a "reality defender" (which is also the name of one of their platforms) that will "collaborate with others and beneficial AI to identify fake media, protect ourselves and society against manipulation, and defend our freedoms."[246] Dr. Deepak Chopra (known as a health and wellbeing expert) is on the foundation's Global Council because they believe that good AI starts with good people.

Roger Spitz, the founder of Techistential, has seen how AI is evolving. According to Spitz, it is gradually moving up the "Decision-Making Value Chain Loop," starting from "Analytical" (with analytics-driven decision support), to "Predictive" (algorithm-augmented decisions), and will gradually begin encroaching on "Prescriptive" decision making. "Advancements in machine learning may mean that we reach a point where strategic decision-making is no longer a human exclusive."[247] One day, critical decisions in the areas of finance, education, architecture, automotive, law, and medicine will be guided or made by AI.

Marketing companies will have to rethink brand storytelling altogether as augmented and virtual reality creates a presence for consumers that two-dimensional technology cannot achieve. Visual mediums may no longer dominate the space because audio-based augmented reality will create a medium of vocal communication between consumers and their device, and therefore with the companies behind those devices. This will create a business model that will require a totally new type of thinking: Business to Robot to Consumer.

Changing Consumer Behaviors

When developing future technologies, companies must consider declining birth rates and aging populations. Businesses count on the young for quick adaptation and use of the technology. For example, the millennial and Gen Z generations both quickly adapted to technology, especially the Internet. Millennials drove businesses online while Gen Z pushed mobile adoption.

A decline in birth rates "also means fewer children requiring products and services ... and therefore, fewer consumers over a lifetime."[248] This is something to keep in mind as "a low birthrate will reduce the working-age population, leading to a decline in production and economic growth."[249] If these trends continue, companies who invest in AI, robotics, and digital human helpers will have the upper hand in keeping their companies going and growing, because these technologies will make up for the deficit in a younger workforce.

From a consumer standpoint, aging populations are living longer in developed countries. This creates a new market for elder-friendly technology. While important, the elderly don't just need assistance that robotics, AI, and spatial computing can offer. A consumer report from Deloitte says that "the key to attracting boomers is appealing to their 'forever young' attitude."[250] Anti-aging products will generate billions of dollars in revenue as well as "brain games offered on mobile devices and web to help boomers stay mentally fit and boost productivity well into old age."[251]

Virtual reality is the perfect tool for augmented consciousness and improving memory. With this in mind, companies would be wise to invest in the elderly as well as younger generations. Technologies and their applications are already so diverse, and there are a myriad of companies competing for market share. This means that tools will be available to reach people of all ages.

Opportunities and Challenges

5G can power new technologies and create an environment for better-connected devices. Each new interaction of network and technology, from microwaves to WiFi, has to prove its value to customers. The lack of understanding around 5G makes it hard for consumers to see the value in it.

This is a perfect example of the type of work companies have set out for them with future technology. It's not going to be as easy as handing out a new cell phone. Companies need to build trust in their products from the data and software level. They need to make it simple and apparent where people's data is distributed and stored, what specific information is shared, and give user-first options to continue with those actions or not, without being annoying.

Tech companies like Instagram, Google, and Facebook believed they were making the world a better place. By using their software and services, people would feel more connected and empowered. Unfortunately, their belief has become controlling, policing their users and forcing their values.[252] These policies alienate many users and will need to be addressed fairly in order to retain ascendancy. Apple and Google updated iOS and Android phones with tracing technology that can be used by government agencies. Advertisers have pulled out of social media platforms like Facebook, Instagram, and Twitter in record numbers amidst the hostile climate these very sites created. Users are deleting their Facebook accounts in record numbers despite Facebook's overall growth.

The good news is that companies of the future can learn from Web 2.0's first-generation stumbles. Now is the chance to halt the dystopian future so many books and movies predict. Most people fear living in an Orwellian world, and therefore businesses would be wise to honor people's desire for freedom, expression, privacy, and equality. Companies who choose to use AR, VR, and AI can make ethical choices around customers' data and actions by implementing cybersecurity values first.

For instance, instead of a ten-page "agreement" that most users swipe through to dismissively "agree to," we suggest clear summaries and interactive media so as to build understanding and trust. When you're voting on a proposition, the ballot will tell you what "Yes" and "No" mean and their implications. Businesses will need to offer the same transparency to their customers.

VR, AR, and AI offer more opportunities for companies than just a chance to reinstate cybersecurity and privacy first protocols. These technologies offer new business models that only digital worlds and AI robots can offer. While virtual words have been playing virtual concerts for over a decade, such as Duran Duran playing a gig within Second Life in 2006,[253] online video games are also getting in on the action. Fortnite, which started as a game in 2017, is a good example. Nowadays, it's much more than just a game. In 2020, nearly 28 million people watched rapper Travis Scott perform within Fortnite.[254] But Epic Games didn't just stream Scott's performance. They built a world with history and depth, a world where people can interact with the environment and each other.[255] In a marketplace where companies compete for eyes across devices, Fortnite may have figured out the next-generation-way to succeed.

As mentioned earlier, companies also have a new type of customer: robots. When people turn to digital assistants and build personal relationships with their augmented reality devices, companies will have the chance to try a different kind of marketing. Enter the business-to-robot-to-consumer (B2R2C) customer journey. Marketing is changing as voice assistants, Artificial Intelligence (AI), drones, and digital avatars become the gatekeepers between brands and consumers. Businesses will market to robots as they become the decision-makers for seemingly trivial tasks in their customers' lives, such as what to eat for dinner, which workout to do, and what medicine to take.[256]

Predictions Near and Mid-Term

Since 2016, as some have called "the birth year of VR,"[257] virtual reality and augmented reality have been just around the corner for mass consumer consumption. With each new headset hitting the market, a similar article would post that "VR is Dead."[258] Despite the mixed messaging behind AR and VR, they both continue to make headway in the marketplace and into the hands of consumers.

The rise of 5G networks "could accelerate the adoption of augmented and virtual reality" since it gives "developers a larger canvas on which to design new experiences."[259] As a visual medium, augmented reality is used most through a smartphone, which, to take advantage of 5G networks, needs to be updated to the latest models. Unfortunately, due to 5G's limitation as a line-of-sight connection, it's "likely that users will lose access if they encounter obstructions such as large buildings when moving."[260] Once this is overcome, adoption of the technology will likely become more widespread.

Even without 5G, augmented reality will continue to flourish on smartphones, augmented headphones, and haptic feedback on smartwatches or other wearable devices. In the mid-term, smart glasses like Apple's infamously rumored ones, will enter the marketplace. For consumers, virtual "try-ons" and virtually displaying furniture in the home are just the beginning. As people's digital lives become more blended with their physical ones, consumers will turn to virtual fashion to spice up their online selves. The more online fashion and digital selves are normalized, the closer the metaverse comes to being reality.

The metaverse won't be a made-up virtual place. It will be our physical world augmented by sights, sounds, smells, and touch. In *Wired*, Kevin Kelly describes a Mirrorworld where "every street, lamppost, building, and room will have its full-size digital twin." AR glasses and apps show bits and pieces of what the Mirrorworld might look like. However, "these virtual fragments are being stitched together to form a shared, persistent place that will parallel the real world."[261]

At the beginning of 2020, a worldwide pandemic swept across countries, disrupting business and social life. Countries went into lockdowns, and social distancing became standard in an effort to curb infection rates. Companies quickly had to shift their employees to work remotely and adopt new methods for keeping in touch with clients. Virtual reality is the tool many are using to communicate and collaborate.

Maor Cohen writes, "Zoom went from 10M users to 300M users in just a few months....As our digital lives become increasingly 3D, it will be essential to ensure these experiences create a sense of presence that promotes the effective exchange of ideas and knowledge. Creating a presence doesn't necessarily require a headset. For example, [an] artificial window concept by Argodesign simulates working next to a colleague—right down to the eye contact—and Virbela is helping previously in-person conferences move to computer-based video-game-like worlds. Meanwhile, companies offering full spatial audio and 3D telepresence solutions, such as Spatial, are building experiences that allow you to participate from a computer as well as VR."[262]

The pandemic is expected to directly impact virtual and augmented reality adoption positively, especially for those working from home and engaged in online shopping. The AR/VR market is expected to grow by $125 billion during 2020–2024.[263] Concerns over COVID-19 make consumers less likely to go into stores, and those who do are reluctant to try on products. Augmented reality can replicate "try-on" experiences, like shoes or make-up, without the potential health risks.

Interfaces are moving beyond the screen, and eventually, smartphones might not be necessary as brain computer interfaces reach the market. Brain–computer interfaces (BCI) read brainwaves and neural reactions that allow people to interact with computers or robots as naturally as looking with their eyes or thinking of an action. BCIs come in all forms, from direct sensors on the brain to headphones, eyeglasses, and wristwatches. These devices represent the future of huma–computer interface, which allows humans to be their most

genuine selves and free up their hands and eyes to engage
with people and the world around them.

Take the Leap

Engaged employees do better work, create a happier
workforce, and are better equipped to satisfy customers.
Tom Symonds, Co-Founder and CEO at Immerse, believes
"every company should be focused on improving its
workforce and enhancing the employee experience, and
technology provides plenty of tools to do this." [264] Virtual
reality will revolutionize the way training is delivered. It
will change how we upskill employees, helping them to
extend their careers in a world of ever-changing technology.
Companies that use the technology we talk about in this
book and deploy it in a way that works for their employees
will see increased engagement, more positive outcomes, and
higher employee retention. "Now is the moment for
companies to start exploring the potential of this technology
to increase employee engagement, productivity and
retention," said Symonds.

Companies who invest in spatial computing and 5G
networks can gain back employee trust. Those that put
cybersecurity first and prove themselves to be ethical, have
a chance to create a whole new market of experiences that
customers have never dreamed of.

Augmented and virtual reality and artificial intelligence
enabled by 5G networks opens a host of new opportunities
for company ROI. "5G is a game-changer for enterprise
VR," said Justin Parry, Co-founder and COO at Immerse.
"Cloud technology means that the power needed for VR
processing can be handled directly by the cloud.... This
accelerates the uptake of enterprise VR and extends the
benefits of this technology to a much wider number of
organizations and employees." [265] Seeing results from this
technology takes more than simply adopting it. It will take
a shift in thinking from hardware and systems up through
creative and customer outreach, as well as training and
investment.

Companies will have to think in three dimensions at first. "Immersive XR technologies such as VR and AR are a key part of this blend, transforming the way we learn, explore and interact," said Symonds. "They can give leaders a competitive edge through higher engagement and better results, and they provide ways of tracking and measuring employee performance that were previously impossible." Spatial computing is the next computing platform. It creates opportunities for knowledge creation and collaboration that humanity has never experienced up until this point.[266] As former Apple CEO, John Sculley said, "The future belongs to those who see the possibilities before they become obvious."[267]

Leading an Augmented Workforce

A phrase that is often attributed to famed American football coach, Vince Lombardi, is "good leaders are made, not born," and this couldn't be more true as we enter an era of hyper-change and accelerated technological advancements. Today's leaders will need to acquire different skills than their predecessors in order to lead because having an augmented workforce reframes what defines a good leader.

From 2010 to 2020, customer experience became a mainstream trend and a business imperative. According to Oracle:[268]

> [C]ustomer experience (CX) refers to how a business engages with its customers at every point of their buying journey—from marketing to sales to customer service and everywhere in between. In large part, it's the sum total of all interactions a customer has with your brand. Customer experience is not just a set of actions. It also focuses on feelings. How do your customers or prospective customers feel about your brand? At every customer touchpoint, you can improve—or destroy—how your customers feel about you. So there are important decisions to make at each touchpoint, and those decisions influence how successful your business will be as a result.

In 2021 and beyond, we wager that *employee* experience (EX) will become as important as customer experience (CX) and technologies like AR, VR and AI will unlock EX's full potential. This puts the employees at the center of what makes an organization successful. A move from only being customer-centric at the expense of employee burnout will shift to organizations needing to both be customer and employee-centric as a business imperative.

The World Economic Forum estimates that by 2025, 85 million jobs may be displaced by a shift in the division of labor between humans and machines.[269] But even more jobs—97 million—may emerge that are more adapted to the new division of labor between humans, machines, and algorithms. Workers will need to augment their skills to fill these roles and businesses will need to provide new and innovative ways for employees to be reskilled and retrained, while also remaining engaged.

According to WEF, the top skills which employers see as rising in prominence in the lead-up to 2025 are:

1. Analytical thinking and innovation

2. Active learning and learning strategies

3. Complex problem-solving

4. Critical thinking and analysis

5. Resilience, stress tolerance, and flexibility

6. Creativity, originality, and initiative

7. Leadership and social influence

8. Reasoning, problem-solving, and ideation

9. Emotional intelligence

10. Technology design and programming

Some of the key questions that arise when leaders think about the augmented workforce include:

- How do you assess your workforce in this new paradigm?
- How do you make an augmented workforce work for your organization?
- Is my organization ready?
- How do we get started?

As more workers need to be upskilled and re-trained than ever before, these technologies will allow them to be trained faster and be better engaged. Also, as Gen Z workers continue to enter the workforce, they will expect companies to be innovative in the way they train them, including gamifying learning and training and using new technologies like AR and VR.

Managing an augmented workforce will bring with it new challenges and opportunities for leaders as rapid technological change collides with demographic shifts in the workforce. In this chapter, we introduce some of the questions you need to start thinking through at your organization. We also present an initial framework for scoping your path toward the future and how to manage an augmented workforce. With great tech comes great resistance. That's why we want to help leaders make the right decisions to get past the resistance.

You will have the early adopters in your organization who are sold on the new technology and eager to get started with it and adapt it into their daily working habits. You will also have the laggards, who are not at all interested in new tech and resist change. Then you have all the employees in between and these are the people you have a chance to convert and who will be critical in making a leader fit for the expansion to come.

CHAPTER TWENTY-FIVE

The Five Commandments of Technology and Business

Many technology books focus on building excitement for the future. This book gives you the tools to act on that excitement. It's about staying focused on what matters most to your business and the correct use of technology so that your company and customers will be served well. This chapter walks through advice and methods for leveraging technologies into meaningful, long-term success for your customers and your company.

Here we share the five commandments of business and technology. We view this chapter as being the medicine many people need to remedy incorrect ways of applying technologies to business. It may sound strange for us to say, "Don't focus on the technologies," in a technology book. But we've seen too many companies misapply various technologies, which led to a massive waste of time and money.

People don't say, "I really need to hammer some nails today." They say, "I need to build a house." You wouldn't wake up and say to yourself, "I need to use my pressure washing equipment this week." You would say, "I need to clean my dirty driveway." People want results, not just technology. The technology, tools, and effort can lead to desired results when there is a harmony between your vision, mission, values, goals, and the correct use of technology.

We want to prevent you from being dazzled or inordinately enamored by technologies so that you use the right ones in the right way for your business. Too many business leaders believe that AI, VR, or AR is the silver bullet. They think these emerging technologies alone are going to solve their problems. In the midst of that pursuit, they lose sight of the customer and their business. We have heard too many business leaders say, "We need an AR strategy." No, you need a customer strategy. If you say, "We need a VR strategy by the end of Q4," that's like walking into a pharmacy and saying, "What's my aspirin strategy?" A pharmacist can't answer that question without knowing your health history, symptoms, diagnosis, and prognosis.

Similarly, once you have a clear plan for your company and customer, you'll know which technology to employ and how to wield it. One technology or device will not solve all of your business problems. That leads us to our first of five commandments for technology and business.

You Shall Not Ask, "Can We?" but "Should We?"

A large soft drink company was about to release a new flavored drink, and they believed augmented reality would be the key to their marketing success. We consulted with them and asked the executives what problem they were trying to solve. They couldn't really answer that question but felt that the way to get customers excited about this new product was by using AR. They seemed to think that it was a silver bullet.

We voiced several concerns. "If you use AR, the customer is going to have to have a certain kind of smartphone or better, and millions of people around the world don't have access to such devices. They'll need to have a bandwidth plan that allows downloads of 3D assets quickly, or it won't work properly. They're going to need to care enough about an unreleased soda that they would spend precious customer time preparing to have this moment." The executives hadn't thought about any of this.

We also asked them to consider that looking at a soda bottle wasn't really entertaining or useful; it was just something people might click on if they were curious. In other words, there wasn't much of an incentive to interact with this product via AR. The question they didn't want to address was, "Will placing a virtual soft drink on a table via AR inspire customers to care? Will this drive them to purchase?"

The AR component wasn't tied to any promotion, and there was hardly any marketing strategy behind this. The company spent hundreds of thousands of dollars for the AR asset, and yet, maybe a few hundred people visited the webpage and used the AR option. It was a failure, but the marketing team wanted to be able to check a box and tell their boss, "Yes, we're using AR." Can they employ AR? Sure. Should they? No. It was a waste of time, energy, and money.

These errors typically happen when the focus is on the technology instead of the company's mission and the customer's experience. While many companies are focused on customer-facing applications, they should also consider how AR could be used for training employees. For example, if you're a bottled water company, instead of coming up with an AR design for your product, a better idea may be to use AR to train employees to lift a pallet properly. This could increase safety, lead to less accidental damage in the bottling plant, lower costs, and increased profits. Some companies are quick to invest hundreds of thousands of dollars in an AR app because they're only thinking about the customer's usage. They've asked, "Can we?" But they haven't asked, "Should we?" And what about the employees? As mentioned above, could AR be better utilized for the workers and not the customers in various situations?

For instance, if someone were going through a stock room with an assistive AR setup such as Google Glass, business intelligence could alert him or her to opportunities to restructure the warehouse layout to make it easier to fulfill orders for popular products. In the future, salespeople or other customer-facing staff could be reminded of products that the customer has bought before or common objections and the answers to them. A company could then leverage the data they gather from all the customers they interact with to drive efficiency, improve profit margins, and improve delivery speed.

Mike Pell, Envisioneer and Director of the Microsoft Garage NYC, shared this hopeful advice: "We are just on the edge of almost anything being possible. We'll be able to create (or accurately simulate) our wildest ideas in relatively no time. Given that, it's critical we ask the key ethical and moral question "should we?" every single time. Ignoring that discussion is turning away from the truth that accomplishing an amazing technological feat (just because we can) may not be the right thing to do for the people side of the equation."

We fell into this trap of focusing on "Can we?" before asking, "Should we?" when we created a holographic press release years ago. While it was innovative, not many people found it exciting to watch somebody talking from different angles. Could we do it? Yes, we did it. Should we have done it? No, we should've thought through the user-experience and realized that this wasn't the best application for holographic imagery. If this were a fashion show, the user would likely want to view the model and clothes from various angles. But, for a press release, it was unnecessary.

Rather than jumping to the conclusion that your company must use AR, consider if the technology could be more of a hindrance than a help for the user experience. If you're trying to choose a mutual fund, does it actually matter if a bar chart pops-up out of the ground using VR technology? It's one thing to have a tremendously compelling technology. But if your customer has to buy a $300 device just to see it, it's likely a non-starter.

Ask yourself a few gut-check questions before moving from "can we" to "should we." For example:

- Will this presentation of data (3D, voice, AR) help or distract employees from the user's task?

- Is this solution cost-effective, and will it increase revenue?

- How easily can customers adopt this?

- Will this technology (AR, VR, XR) produce useful business intelligence data?

- Does this technology solve a customer pain point?

- Will this new tool introduce new problems for the customers or the company to overcome?

- Is this strategy safe and reliable in the short term and long term?

- Even if implementing this new technology is possible, is it something that our customers truly need (or want) and will use?

The point is, before jumping on any bandwagon, you must assess whether your tool or idea is best for your business and customers. Don't ask, "Can we?"—but ask, "Should we?"

You Shall Ignore Hardware

Ignore hardware. At least in business, don't be married to it. We shouldn't focus on devices right now because whatever we're looking at today will be a proverbial paperweight in just a little while. Companies that think they're building the state-of-the-art today are often outmoded in a quarter or two. The new headset with an upgraded battery life will come out shortly. An updated cell phone will drop each year. In a matter of months, 4K will become 8K. Because vast change can occur within less than a year, it's best to focus on storytelling and employees' needs instead of on hardware. Focus on education for employees so they understand the new technologies and don't feel threatened by them. Let employees demo the tech before it is deployed and put systems in place for employee feedback. Once programs are rolled out, use these feedback loops as ways for employees to air out grievances.

Experts agree that there will be mass adoption of AI, XR, and 5G. The question is, "How soon?" The best way to prepare is to focus on the new opportunities these technologies create. For example, all of the above technologies will improve ways to understand employees better, faster, and with more confidence. Businesses can prepare for the future by thinking through how to leverage that information since the analytics will create new possibilities that could significantly transform a business or business model.

The landscape is changing rapidly as hardware manufacturers struggle to keep up with the change. Do not be tied down to one device or system. One company tried to invent a case with a physical keyboard that could be added to an iPhone. The trouble was that by the time they finished the specifications and manufacturing for one model, a new iPhone came out with a different size screen. The company went under because it was never able to launch a case that matched the newest model. While they believed that they could keep up with the latest versions of the iPhone, they couldn't create a case for an iPhone which came out seven years ago nor any version since then.

Take 5G as an example. While an app designer may be quick to build for 5G, he or she needs to keep in mind that there'll be issues related to coverage, device availability, data pricing, battery life, and weight for the foreseeable future. Before putting all your eggs in the 5G basket, it's essential to recognize that widespread consumer adoption and carrier coverage maps take time.

When John led the team that created the AR configurator for Porsche, we let customers configure their purchase, something they could only do in a showroom. So, we made the AR configurator for the iPad and iPhone instead of the HoloLens because that was the device that customers were likely to have on them instead of one that was expensive or that they may not always carry with them. And in the process, we were able to gather data on the popular angles, models, colors, and features of the car.

All of this informed future sales and marketing activities for the company. We focused on goals rather than hardware so that we could deliver results using what's available and widespread. As Jeff Bezos says, invest in the things that don't change as much.[270] And customers don't change much. That leads us to the third commandment.

You Shall Focus on the Customer

Long-lasting success can exist in companies that understand customers have problems and remember that technology is only a tool to solve their problems. Getting out into the field to understand the customer's needs is essential. Get as close to the customer as possible. Consult the customer and customer-facing employees about design and pain points so you know what to create, change, or improve. Frequently, businesses make decisions or changes without any input from customers, and it ends up being completely divorced from reality.

Once we had the opportunity to work with a multimillion-dollar global company that makes pavers and concrete used to build luxury backyards with patios, a fireplace, a fire pit, and other amenities. Sometimes this company sells tens of thousands of dollars in concrete products for a job like this. Their designers would take pictures on site and then send those pictures and specifications to a design studio, which would then render a 3D model for the customer to view using prints.

However, this process would take several days—from when the salesperson was on site, to design, to printing, to setting up another appointment, to the salesperson returning to show the design. None of this was done in real-time. Sometimes, the salesperson would return and speak with one member of the family, only to hear that they wanted to show the design to their spouse (who wasn't home at the time), which slowed down the process even further. It required a third trip.

Visualization was vital for customers. They couldn't imagine what their backyard would look like with the changes. Without some kind of visualization, it didn't seem worth the cost. However, the company found that after customers saw the images, they would close on 90 percent of the leads. Unfortunately, due to the long turnaround time, only 10 percent of the sales team used the 3D images.

This company had heard about our work with AR, and we consulted with them. We spent a full day with various leaders, listening, and asking questions. We asked, "What if the customer didn't have to wait a week to see their rendering? What if the salesperson didn't have to schedule another appointment and go back out to the customer? What if you could do all that you're already doing on the spot?" They said, "That sounds very interesting."

We explained that the salespeople could use augmented reality. They could work on a tablet, so it would be easy for everyone involved to see the design simultaneously and make changes in real-time. The leadership loved the idea, especially since only 10 percent of the salespeople used the 3D rendering option. They needed the other 90 percent of the sales team to adopt the same practice.

The people we talked with believed that the AR route could be the perfect solution to this dilemma, but the deal fell apart. Why? Because when they presented this plan to the executives and financial decision-makers, they were too focused on the plan's technological aspects. They didn't share enough about the customer's needs and the possible profits. This solution would have increased their top-line revenue by nearly 2,000 percent, yet the executives were so concerned about getting everyone on board with AR that they missed out on how this would help customers and close more sales.

The lesson to learn is that whether you're dealing directly with the customer or putting together a proposal for your boss, stay focused on the customer. Don't share too much tech jargon. Talk about increased efficiency, revenue growth, and customer satisfaction. Don't try to dazzle people with technology (at least, not in overly technical terms). Demonstrate the best customer care that you can and let the technology do the work.

Businesses have gone on too many buzzword boondoggles that forget the customer. "I heard that VR is the way to go. Let's get something going." That's not a plan. You will need to do gut-checks daily. Ask yourself if you're doing the project because it's cool or because it's useful.

We have seen millions of dollars wasted on a "go big or go home" mentality, too. Leaders will say, "We need to get a jump on the competition. We have to roll out our AR solution." That kind of thinking can create a plethora of problems. Start small. Be agile. You don't need the biggest and the best. Sometimes, something ugly and functional is better than a beautiful nothing—a nothing due to a grandiose idea that goes nowhere. You shall focus on the customer.

Go out into the field and make sure that you're asking customers key questions, such as:

- We think you're having trouble with this. Is that true?

- What do you like or dislike about this product?

- We're thinking about spending money to improve this. Does that sound right? Or would you rather us focus on another part of the program/product?

- Do you need speed, effectiveness, reduced costs, or something else?

- Would (fill-in-the-blank with the latest technology) be something that would enhance your experience with our product?

- Would you be willing to test a beta version of this product?

You Shall Learn from Your Failures

A quote commonly attributed to Thomas Edison says, "I have not failed. I've just found 10,000 ways that don't work."[271] You're going to fail. That's part of the process. You fail so that you can eventually succeed. Failure, when done correctly, leads to the right answer or to develop something unique and useful. If you knew the answer or solution, you'd succeed on the first try. But, that rarely happens. So, don't be afraid to fail. Failure is data, and data is always useful. Therefore, heed the fourth commandment: You shall learn from your failures.

At the end of any project it's important to identify lessons learned. Different project methodologies do this in different ways. Agile Scrum completes retrospectives throughout the project. Traditional project management conducts lessons learned with project managers, team members, and leadership. Lessons learned starts with identifying what went well, what did not go well, and what could be improved. The session is about identifying the project's successes and failures. This can be done by breaking the project into categories such as resources, project management, technical support, etc.

Once lessons learned are identified, they should be officially documented to share with everyone involved on the project. Project management can then analyze the results to identify any process improvements or training needed as a result of the lessons learned. Save the lessons learned in a way where they can be accessed for future projects. Remember, finding what doesn't work is just as valuable as finding what does work. And that means feeling free to fail.

We believe there's an institutional bias against failure. It may come from the olden days of a manufacturing economy when you had to throw out valuable materials when you made a mistake. If you messed up while making a pair of shoes, that failure cost the company a good deal of money. We should build in more room to experiment and even fail. Besides being inheritors of a manufacturing economy, it's also true that people don't like to fail; it hurts our pride. But the reality is that when dealing with technology, the process will include trial and error.

A great example of turning a failure into a success is the work that Jonathan Moss, former head of Learning and Development, has done at Sprint. He trained employees but felt that the training was tedious, expensive, and ineffective. Sprint would send people out to the Midwest to endure hours of classroom training, but not everyone remembered what they had learned. It simply didn't move the needle—product knowledge and sales didn't increase.

So, Jonathan and team put all the training for the phones they sold on employee's phones so all of the customer sales talking points would hang off the products in augmented reality for their training. Suddenly, not only did the salespeople use this to train on, but they then used it with the customers. They subsequently put some of this data on the store's sample phones for customers to use themselves.

It was so effective that Sprint didn't need as many salespeople for the same store. They saved money on training and sold more phones. It all began because Jonathan Moss was willing to find new solutions in past failings. Had he feared looking at the company's mistakes or was scared to report the previous program's ineffectiveness, he would have never come up with a fantastic solution. Jonathan is an excellent example of following the commandment: You shall learn from your failures.

Be ready to fail and then let the company know what failed so that others can learn. If you're a leader, build a culture of "freedom to fail" in your company so that it can learn crucial lessons. There is tremendous value in sharing your failures because you're letting others know what didn't work, thus saving them time and energy.

It may be more accurate to say that these situations aren't "failures," but things that did not work or work best. A project might fail, a new product might not catch on, but these may be valuable learning experiences to help the company or team move forward toward greater success. We suggest that project teams ask these critical questions at the end of any venture:

- What questions should we have asked that we didn't (and that we will ask in the future)?

- Despite an undesired outcome, did you make the process better, faster, or cheaper?

- Did you have a plan from the cradle to the grave for your project?

- What went right, and what went wrong?

- How could we have better prepared for this project?

- How did it affect customer satisfaction? Were customers happier? Why or why not?

- Were people better off?

- Can this idea grow?

- What does this failure mean for the customer and the company? What should we be focusing on or doing instead?

You Shall Find the Right Partner to Grow With

If you're a company that needs to work on an AI or AR project, it's unlikely that you'll hire a team for this, only to lay them off in a few months. Typically, a company will work with another company or vendor that specializes in a given technological field. Unfortunately, buyers can get distracted by dazzling slide decks. So, they end up in an undesirable partnership that can be disastrous.

Many technology firms may be skilled in delivering an application, but they may not understand how the business they're building for works. Good tech vendors understand how technology can impact an entire company. They work with you to develop an implementation strategy as part of the project deliverables. That's why the fifth commandment is so important: You shall find the right partner to grow with.

We have seen companies make the following mistake too many times. They'll ask, "What's our AR strategy?" and then say, "We should create an app so customers can do something fun on their phone related to our product. What's our budget? Who does AR in our area? Let's pick them."

But, they fail to ask, "Has this group done other work in our industry? Can they talk about the process and not just the output?" Your tech partner should be able to talk about the return on investment they created throughout the process of working with others (this could be an insight, organizational realignment, or money saved). People are quick to grasp what they think is "cool" or trendy for a project, but "cool" can deliver what's needed for your business as a whole.

You'll need to ask your potential technology partner about their expertise and how they helped companies implement previous projects. They should provide reviews from other customers and references. Don't get dazzled by a tech vendor's pitch. Dig deeper and see if they know how your industry or how your business works and how to help you with your specific company and customers.

What should you look for in a partner? You should seek a team that is:

- Stable
- Trustworthy
- Capable
- Secure
- Scalable

A team that can grow your business with a particular technology will need to have extensive experience with it. Without in-depth, hands-on experience, they won't have all the kinks worked out in their services or their product. Without that stability, they won't be able to help you as they'll need to help themselves first. This potential partner needs to be trustworthy, as well. Ask them about the long-term relationships they have and if they can share information on their clients with you.

Your potential technology vendor needs to show that they are capable. Ask how many similarly sized projects they've shipped from beginning to end. Ask how they handle confidential company and customer data. Ask how they help companies implement new technology with a holistic strategy.

Look for a partner that will be able to meet the needs of your company as you grow. A good partner educates their client. They walk through the steps to complete the project. Once the technology is developed, a good tech partner is there to help implement it and support it for a time post Go Live. Are they able to supply what procurement and legal require? When dealing with larger companies, vendors must show they have proper governance, insurance, and security protocols to complete projects without putting their clients at risk. Many emerging tech startups either can't meet or fake answers to these questions.

Do they have the cash to finish your project if there are delays? Larger company procurement departments sometimes ask vendors to provide evidence of a robust business, reporting or showing past financial statements to ensure they won't go out of business if there are payment or project delays. They also sometimes require vendors to submit to long payment delays (e.g., net 90, net 180, etc.). Many emerging tech startups are not ready for work at this level, but they get projects because there are no other providers. Companies should look for ways to support these vendor projects to reduce risk for their own company. Many tech groups can talk a lot of game, but that doesn't mean they can deliver. Look at their track record and look carefully.

Here are seven key questions to ask when assessing how to use technology to help augment your workforce:

1. What are my employees' current attitudes toward these technologies?

2. Do they see AR, VR, and AI as a threat or as a complement to the work they do?

3. Who within my organization are early adopters of this technology and can help evangelize it?

4. How can I make sure my employees get upskilled and retrained faster and, in turn, help my organization continue to innovate and grow?

5. How do I as a leader help lead innovate and change negative attitudes toward technology?

6. What skills does my workforce need to optimize processes and be more efficient?

7. What skills do I need as a leader to remain relevant and productive in this era of change?

After asking these questions, leaders would benefit from using the framework below to begin implementing what they've learned in this book within their organization:

The Augmented Workforce Implementation Framework

By Cathy Hackl and John Buzzell

*1. **Assess** - Evaluate your organization's current use of AR, AI, and 5G and current employees' attitudes towards new technologies.*

*2. **Strategize** - Taking the assessment information and the organization's goals, create a human-centered strategy focused on allowing workers to accept new technologies and optimize process for the organization.*

*3. **Evangelize** - Ask early adopters to help evangelize the strategy with other employees across the organization and generate a mechanism for employees to get their questions answered. Allow employees to learn about these technologies and get hands-on with them before deploying solutions.*

*4. **Implement** - Deploy strategy within the organization*

*5. **Evaluate** - Measure and evaluate employee attitudes after strategy is deployed, then iterate.*

This framework is provided as a starting point for the road ahead, where technology will continue to be critical to processes and will become even more important for workforce success in the decade ahead.

There's an old saying: "Measure twice, cut once." This idea was first used in woodworking or metalworking settings. It means, "Be cautious. Plan, prepare. Be thorough in the beginning so that you save time later." Take time to find the right partner to grow with, or else you'll regret it later. After working on more than a hundred technology projects, we can tell you that there is much wisdom in this maxim.

People get dazzled by a fad, skip processes, don't think through their ideas, or "get in bed" with the wrong partner, and then they're dissatisfied with the results. People lose sight of the fact that they're in business to serve customers, and technology is just a tool to that end. They can hastily jump on the bandwagon just to do "the latest thing," but have no real strategy and then end up wasting money. But, if you plan carefully, and if you vet a tech vendor with the right questions, you'll end up only having to "cut once."

We hope these five commandments can help you steer your experiments with these technologies toward success. It's easy to become dazzled by new things and to use them for technology's sake. With this advice in mind, you should be able to stay focused on your customer's success, and in so doing, achieve your own.

CHAPTER TWENTY-SIX

Seeing the Future, with Fresh Eyes
by John Buzzell

Famed science fiction author William Gibson once said, "The future is already here—it's just not evenly distributed." Exponential technologies like AI, XR, and 5G are spreading quickly. If you have access to one or more of these technologies, the door to your future has swung open wide. If you don't, now you know where to start looking.

This tech is erasing some of the obstacles that have held people back in the past, whether it's a lack of education, poor access to employment, living too far from their dream job, a deficiency in skills, or a scarcity of experience. With a distributed workforce that comes with "just-in-time-training" from augmented reality and AI delivered with 5G (sometimes with edge computing), then suddenly, all of us can be experts.

The future is easy to see if you look in the right places. As we've learned, AI can help with increasing demands for digital interaction and decision-making. AI is already finishing our sentences (Gmail just did that for me today). AR is increasingly adjusting our reality to fit the one we want to have. 5G is delivering it sharper, faster, and cheaper than before. Our growing desire to be more digital while on-the-go can be helped by 5G. The need to enhance or replace physical human contact can be met with visual augmentations and XR.

The younger generation is already talking to each other through animojis or avatars. Reality to them has always been enhanced by or synthesized through digital platforms. We may all be intermediating through digital means in the future. Countless augmentations will be available to enhance your personal and business interactions, leveling the playing field.

AI can use voices and speech patterns to communicate with people who prefer different sounds and styles. If a client is more comfortable speaking with a woman, my device could theoretically transform my virtual face and voice to communicate more effectively to close the deal. Other augmentations could make you sound younger, older, more educated, from a different region of the world, or even more polite. Making a pitch to a client in Germany will be much easier since AI will translate my words and even tailor them to fit the listener's personality. AI could make you sound more assertive or blunt your straightforwardness because it will have its own research of what your client prefers to hear. We may start off with animojis but will end up in virtual reality all the time in the future—able to be and do much more than with the limitations of our physical selves.

The deadly COVID-19 pandemic has led to unprecedented changes in 2020 and beyond, and unprecedented technological advancements have made many positive changes possible. When I was growing up, a video chat was something you only saw in a *Jetsons* cartoon, and most children didn't think they'd be able to communicate like that during their lifetimes. At the moment, Zoom meetings and working remotely are commonplace, sometimes even tedious! What's more, it was inconceivable that video conversations could occur through a portable device, untethered from a large computer at home. Yet today, people of all ages walk around "Facetiming" all over the world.

Long before COVID-19 hit, companies were rethinking their position on remote workers, marketing communications, commercial real estate (including renting shared workspaces), and which tools were best for online collaboration and productivity. Life and work will likely change in some permanent ways, and companies will need to adjust to or accept this "new normal." Various companies are already giving their workers stipends to invest in better webcasting resources (cameras, lights, microphones, faster Internet speeds) because they know this "new normal" may last for quite some time.

Let's consider how these technologies can work together in our post-pandemic reality. A remodeling consultation is happening between a chatbot and a customer, and using AR in a customer's home instead of a showroom. The customer can preview five different couches with their phone, in streaming photorealistic 3D graphics. This one experience is enabled by 5G, AI, XR, which have never been more significant. How will this affect your business? Now you know enough to begin thinking how you'll apply them yourself, grabbing a hold of our shared uncertain future and turning it towards your solid business results!

We are in a period of behavioral transition, and the technology adoption has been supercharged by our socially-distant reality during the pandemic. The world is changing rapidly, and you need to consider that if you aren't creating your own situation, someone else will. You may need to change your work or personal life to adapt to the changes that AI, XR, and 5G technologies are producing.

After reading this book, you're now prepared to start leveraging the possibilities offered by AR, VR, AI, IoT, and 5G networks. There are many opportunities across all industries for quick wins as well as broad successes. Reading this book is the first step to transformational change. I hope that you'll continue exploring and learning. Take the leap in augmenting your organization, and join Cathy and me on social media as we continue our journeys. There is still so much to learn and do. See you in the future!

Acknowledgments

From Cathy

Abundance is my word for 2021, and I have gratitude in abundance to so many that have helped me along the way and with this book:

- To John for going on this book-writing journey with me. Despite several misses, we finally have a win. Thank you for being more than a co-author—thank you for being a friend, career "coach," former boss, fellow XR geek, and a person who has championed me every step of the way.

- To Brian Solis for saying yes to writing our foreword. I'll be forever grateful.

- To Lee Black and Maria Floros for all your help with our book.

- Massive thanks to our editor and secret weapon, Lily Snyder. You are brilliance.

- To Rob Crasco and Navah Berg for all your research and help.

- To Jason—thank you for your patience and for being my helpmate.

- To my kiddos—gratitude for the smiles, snuggles. I'm proud to be your mommy.

- To my parents, thank you. You are my rocks.

- To my brother, sister-in-law, and niece—thanks for believing in me and making me smile.

- To Great-Grandmom and Aunt Martha for being kind and understanding.

- To my friends at Immerse, Avatar Dimension, and Zebra Partners—so much gratitude for asking me to come over and help you grow.

- To Sandy Carter for reaching out when I most needed it. Thank you to Sandy, Amy Belcher, and Joanna Raitano for your leadership during my time at AWS.

- To my Women in XR Friday's group—thank you for helping me during this pandemic. It's nice to know you ladies are always there. Thanks, Joanna Popper, for being our fearless leader.

- To Samantha G. Wolfe for your friendship and for many amazing convos. Thanks for being my first co-author.

- To Iraida Rivas for all the hard work and for helping me with my kiddos so I could get all of this done.

- To Tina Tuli and Rony Abovitz for hiring me at Magic Leap. Every day, I wake up missing my work at Magic Leap. Once a Leaper, always a Leaper.

- To Johnathan Sutherlin and Alvin Wang Graylin— it was a pleasure working with you at HTC VIVE.

- To Andrew "Boz" Bosworth for inspiring me with your talk at the HBS Tech Conf in 2020, and to Ha Thai for considering me for the job of my dreams at Facebook. I got so close.

- To Lisa Kotecki from Facebook Horizon for inviting me to enter the early metaverse.

- To Marty Swant, my editor at Forbes, for giving me a place to bring fresh (and sometimes crazy) ideas to the masses.

- To Amy Webb, for inviting me to join you on Mondays. To Mark Palatucci and Leah Zaidi, for all the great signals.

- To Lt. Col. Jake Sotiriadis for making me a better futurist. Looking forward to the future.

- To Roger Spitz for your insight and advice.

- To Leslie Shannon for all the future-focused conversations.

- To Gaspar Ferreiro for always being there for me.

- To Lisi Linares for all the HacklLisi love.

- To Robyn Stevens for all the PR brilliance.

- To Rani Mani for being my Chief Empathy Officer and for inviting me to be a part of the Adobe Insiders Group.

- To Dr. Ai for all your help and guidance. Magic happens outside our comfort zone.

- To Reinaldo, Nacho, and Beto from UXRTech for being brilliant at XR development.

- To Elizabeth Baron, Julie Smithson, Nate Fender, Sophia Moshasha, Rosario B. Casas, Mariana Acuna Costa, Ashley Crowder, Alan Smithson, Alex Golberg, Cortney Harding, Joachim Scholz, James Ashley, Micah Shippee, Alex Coulombe for your contributions to this book.

- To everyone else I didn't have a chance to thank, thank you. You know who you are.

From John

I couldn't begin to thank anyone without starting with my wife and best friend. She's spent nearly half of her life patiently waiting ("just one minute!") for me to finish something involving technology, whether it was finishing yet another technology project for work or staying up late to chase new experiences in virtual worlds. Other times, she was patiently listening as I practiced how to explain why the thing I was working on currently was the coolest thing ever. This project has consumed nights, weekends, days off, casual conversations, and more. For twenty years, she's cheered me on. I am humbled and eternally grateful. Thank you, Rebecca.

This journey started in March of 2019 as a robot was delivering our lunch at Atlanta's Big Bang Pizza. My good friend and erstwhile futurist-in-residence, Cathy, was excited to do a book together—one that leveraged our experience to help people wield emerging technologies for business. This project has seen its fair share of distractions, including job changes and interstate moves, not to mention a global pandemic. Through it all, Cathy, you've remained dedicated. Your positivity, resilience, resourcefulness, and support are the reasons people have this book in your hands. What's next?

The reason I had any experience to offer on this project started with my parents. If my mother hadn't won a Texas Instruments TI-99/AA computer in a PTA raffle in 1981, and then subsequently given it to me, my life likely would have taken a different path. They fed my obsession with trips to my fifth-grade computer club, long drives to the nearest computer store, and endless floppies, videogames, computer parts, as well as monstrous phone bills from all that late night BBSing. Thanks, Mom and Dad. I owe you both so much.

Across multiple technology transformations (PCs, Narrowband, Broadband, Mobile, Social, XR, and more), my experience has been guided by people and their products. Here are a few of the many to whom I am indebted.

From early days, when I would carefully holepunch Elephant memory 5 ¼ floppies to write data to both sides from my Apple //e, to 2017, when my innovation team summoned an augmented reality Porsche 911 from a humble iPhone 7, Apple Computer, Inc. has inspired my creative potential with its products, people, and technologies. Thanks to everyone from 1 Infinite Loop and beyond.

Thanks to David Kaufman at the University of Georgia School of Art, who allowed me to help set up its first computer lab, spend countless hours accessing the early Internet in 1992–1993, and learn and teach about early creative tools on Macintosh Quadra 700s and 840AVs. Thank you, too, for teaching me and my classmates 3D modeling and animation on Silicon Graphics Iris workstations that must have been impossibly expensive at the time. Most of all, thank you for suggesting that Stephanie Calabrese take a chance on this nerdy kid for a Quality Assurance job testing CD-ROMs. To both of you, thanks for giving me that all-important kickstart to my career.

Since then, there are too many people to thank for opportunities and more. Adam Hunger was my first professional creative partner, who listened as we first discussed the Metaverse on a cold spring night outside the gas station on Peachtree Street in 1992. I still remember excitedly discussing that vision of a MacOS user handing a digital 3D object to a PC user in real time. It was an amazing conversation, and it feels like the future is finally catching up!

Speaking of the Metaverse in the 1990s, when Dave and Buster's wasn't getting all my lunch money for Dactyl Nightmare VR, I was spending my free time poring over dog-eared copies of *Neuromancer, Snowcrash, Microserfs*, Howard Rheingold's *Virtual Reality*, and more. *Wired* magazine was kindling my imagination of what the future could be. I would stay up late studying VRML from Mark Pesce and Tony Parisi and trying to extrapolate from their early work.

There were so many people who helped my career along the way. I'm grateful to colleagues Jim Haleblian, Steve Carlisle,

224 · CATHY HACKL AND JOHN BUZZELL

Bucky Wall, and Peg and Michael Griffith, and the team at Crawford Multimedia, for treating me like one of the guys while I was still a rookie. I owe a lot to Rob Metcalf, early Internet entrepreneur extraordinaire and friend. Michael Adamson, we have a creative partnership that has endured for more than 25 years. Thanks, Michael—we covered a lot of innovation firsts together. The same goes for you other wonderful Turner Broadcasting alumni. Thank you for your partnership and advice, Phil Sharpe, Drew Reifenberger, Robert Occhialini, and Peter Scott. Who knew that someone who doesn't like sports could have so much fun on the starting grid, inside the ropes, or courtside?

As I left Turner to start a business, I learned so much from the partnership and brotherhood I found with Monty Mullig. Thanks, Monty, for showing me how to run a business, and trusting me to help you scale it. We'll always have the Tidewater Cafe at DCA. As we grew, we added so many smart people to the team. Rhonda Lowry, thanks for keeping me honest ("You don't really know that. Do you?"). Adam Sharpe, it was a great journey from *Halo* in the basement to Vice President. Thanks to Chip Silvey, Josh Faubel, Sean Hall, and Zared Redding for helping us build one of the most powerful small teams in XR. Ricardo Olivo, you have been one of the best friends and collaborators of my entire life. I've never worked alongside someone with more grit, inventiveness, and determination, and I'm still amazed at what we've accomplished together. I look forward to seeing all your well-deserved successes.

Together, our team worked with a lot of great clients: Scott Doyne, Heather Turney-Navaei, Damiean Lumsden, Alan Kennedy, Sonia McCollum, and most of all, Lynette Clayton. Thank you for dreaming together with us!

Lily Snyder, you have my enduring gratitude. Your energy and talent have helped make this project a success. Thanks for showing up at exactly the right time to help us finish the book! To Lee, Maria, and the team at Renown Publishing, thanks for your patient guidance and support.

I'd like to offer my sincere and humble thanks to the women in technology I've been lucky enough to collaborate with since 1991: smart, energetic, and kind people like Stephanie Calabrese, Peg Griffith, Marcy Leamy, Linda Sellheim, Rhonda Lowry, Amy Lloyd, Sherri Glass, Andrea Chan, Farah Spainhour, Samantha Wolfe, Julie Smithson, and last but certainly not least, my co-author, Cathy Hackl. You are surely too few and far between. To my beautiful daughters, full of curiosity and passion: you have amazing opportunities ahead that were built from the hard work of your sisters around the world.

Finally, I'd like to thank you, the reader, for working to understand the technologies that will shape our lives for decades to come. Cathy and I wrote this book to be an accessible and friendly way for business leaders to begin to grasp these technologies and put them to work. I applaud you for taking this first step.

See you in the future!

References

1. The Metaverse is a collective term for shared virtual spaces, like virtual worlds. See: Metaverse Roadmap. "20. Glossary." http://metaverseroadmap.org/inputs4.html#glossary.

2. Hanger Clinic. "Featured Technology: Hanger Clinic ExoSym." October 30, 2019. https://hangerclinic.com/blog/featured-technology/hanger-clinic-exosym/.

3. Diamandis, Peter H., and Steven Kotler. *The Future Is Faster Than You Think: How Converging Technologies Are Transforming Business, Industries, and Our Lives*. Simon & Schuster, 2020, p. 7-8.

4. Shah Mbe, Vikas. "A Conversation with Peter Diamandis on How Technology Is Transforming Every Aspect of Our Lives." Thought Economics, January 17, 2020. https://thoughteconomics.com/peter-diamandis.

5. Shah Mbe, "A Conversation with Peter Diamandis."

6. Edwards, David. "Amazon Now Has 200,000 Robots Working in Its Warehouses." Robotics and Automation News, January 21, 2020. https://roboticsandautomationnews.com/2020/01/21/amazon-now-has-200000-robots-working-in-its-warehouses/28840/.

7. Snyder, Lily. "Virtual Reality: Digitally Disrupting Location-based Conferences." April 27, 2018. https://lilyotron.blog/2018/04/27/merging-realities-digitally-disrupting-location-based-conferences/.

8. Zielinsky, Dave. "A New Era in Presentation." *Toastmasters Magazine*, 2018, p. 22. https://toastmasterscdn.azureedge.net/medias/

files/department-documents/magazine/magazine-pdfs/2018-maga-zine-pdfs/web-full-issue-r-0218.pdf.

9. Swisher, Kara. "How Will Tech Help in a Time of Pandemic?" *The New York Times*, February 27, 2020. https://www.ny-times.com/2020/02/27/opinion/coronavirus-tech-facebook.html.

10. Duboff, Rori. "Virtual Reality in the Time of COVID-19." Accenture, April 15, 2020. https://www.accenture.com/us-en/blogs/interactive-insights-blog/virtual-reality-in-the-time-of-covid-19.

11. Oculus Business. "Empowering a Sales Team to Become Top Dog." https://business.oculus.com/case-studies/nestle.

12. Symphony Retail. "Nestlé Purina PetCare Sees Virtual Reality as Innovative Lever." symphonyretailai.com/knowledge-hub/nestle-pu-rina-petcare-sees-virtual-reality-as-innovative-lever/.

13. Symphony Retail, "Nestlé Purina PetCare Sees Virtual Reality as Innovative Lever."

14. Greenwold, Simon. "Spatial Computing." MIT Graduate Thesis, 2013. https://acg.media.mit.edu/people/simong/thesis/SpatialCom-puting.pdf.

15. Hackl, Cathy. "The Country Club of the Future." Forbes, November 15, 2020. https://www.forbes.com/sites/cathyhackl/2020/11/15/the-country-club-of-the-future.

16. "Oculus Facebook Horizon." https://www.oculus.com/facebook-horizon/. Accessed September 17, 2020.

17. Snyder, Lily. "Why People Dislike Social VR (and How to Make It Better)." September 13, 2017. https://lilyotron.blog/2017/09/13/why-people-dislike-social-vr-and-how-to-make-it-better/

18. Rubin, Peter. "Disney's New *Lion King* Is the VR-Fueled Future of Cinema." Wired, July 18, 2019. https://www.wired.com/story/dis-ney-new-lion-king-vr-fueled-future-cinema.

19. Bernard, Zoë. "Jeff Bezos' Advice to Amazon Employees is to Stop Aiming for Work-Life 'Balance'—Here's What You Should Strive for Instead." Business Insider, January 9, 2019.

https://www.businessinsider.com/jeff-bezo-advice-to-amazon-employees-dont-aim-for-work-life-balance-its-a-circle-2018-4.

20. DXC Technology. "The Digital Twin: Data-driven Simulations Innovate the Manufacturing Process." https://assets1.dxc.technology/analytics/downloads/DXC-Analytics-Digital-Twin.pdf.

21. Fellowes, Inc. "Meet Emma Our Work Colleague of the Future." https://www.fellowes.com/gb/en/resources/fellowes-introduces/work-colleague-of-the-future.aspx.

.22 Fellowes, Inc. "Meet Emma."

23 Houser, Kristin. "This Creepy Life-Sized Doll Is a Warning About What Office Life Is Doing to Us." Science Alert, October 28, 2019. https://www.sciencealert.com/this-representation-of-the-next-generation-s-office-worker-is-terrifying.

24. Houser, "This Creepy Life-Sized Doll."

25. Houser, "This Creepy Life-Sized Doll."

26. Shekhar, S., and P. Vold. "Spatial Computing." MIT Press, 2020. https://mitpress.mit.edu/books/spatial-computing.

27. Gribetz, Meron. "A Glimpse of the Future Through an Augmented Reality Headset." TED Conferences, February 2016. https://www.ted.com/talks/meron_gribetz_a_glimpse_of_the_future_through_an_augmented_reality_headset.

28. Diamandis, P. H., and S. Kotler. *The Future Is Faster Than You Think: How Converging Technologies Are Transforming Business, Industries, and Our Lives.* Simon & Schuster, p. 64.

29. Wong, Marcus. "Solved: What Is Protopia?" December 5, 2018. https://marcuswkwong.com/the-concept-of-protopia.

30. Wong, "Solved: What Is Protopia?"

31. Sculley, John. *Moonshot.* RosettaBooks, 2014.

32. Schwartz, Jeff. "Get Ready for the Augmented Workforce." *The Wall Street Journal,* May 10, 2017. https://deloitte.wsj.com/cio/2017/05/10/get-ready-for-the-augmented-workforce/.

33. Rotman, David. "We're Not Prepared for the End of Moore's Law." MIT Technology Review, February 24, 2020. https://www.technologyreview.com/2020/02/24/905789/were-not-prepared-for-the-end-of-moores-law/.

34. Robertson, Adi, and Michael Zelenko, eds. "Voices from a Virtual Past: An Oral History of a Technology Whose Time Has Come Again." The Verge. https://www.theverge.com/a/virtual-reality/oral_history.

35. Motte, Stefanie. "Augmented Reality: A Comprehensive History (Part 1)." Vertebrae, June 18, 2018. https://www.vertebrae.com/blog/history-augmented-reality-1/.

36. Motte, "Augmented Reality."

37. University of Washington College of Engineering. "Thomas A. Furness." Accessed July 1, 2020. https://ise.washington.edu/facultyfinder/thomas-a-furness.

38. Fisher, Adam. *Valley of Genius: The Uncensored History of Silicon Valley (as Told by the Hackers, Founders, and Freaks Who Made It Boom)*. Hachette Book Group, 2018.

39. Fisher, *Valley of Genius.*

40. Zimmerman, K. A., and J. Emspak. "Internet History Timeline: ARPANET to the World Wide Web." Live Science, June 27, 2017. https://www.livescience.com/20727-Internet-history.html.

41. Blank, Steve. "The Secret History of Silicon Valley." p. 151. https://steveblank.com/secret-history.

42. Fisher, *Valley of Genius,* p. 153.

43. Fisher, *Valley of Genius,* p. 152.

44. Quinn, Karl. "Lawnmower Man, 'First' Virtual Reality Film, to Be Remade in Virtual Reality." *The Sydney Morning Herald,* January 23, 2017. https://www.smh.com.au/entertainment/movies/lawnmower-man-first-virtual-reality-film-to-be-remade--in-virtual-reality-20170123-gtwrj1.html.

45. Robertson and Zelenko, "Voices from a Virtual Past."

46. Command International Pictures. "Power of Glove." https://thepowerofglove.com.

47. Chandler, Nathan. "How the Nintendo Power Glove Worked." How Stuff Works. https://electronics.howstuffworks.com/nintendo-power-glove1.htm.

48. Chandler, "How the Nintendo Power Glove Worked."

49. Betters, Elyse. "Google Glass: A Brief History." Pocket-lint, 2015. https://www.pocket-lint.com/ar-vr/news/google/132399-google-glass-a-brief-history.

50. Weidner, Justin Burton. "How and Why Google Glass Failed." Investopedia, March 8, 2020. https://www.investopedia.com/articles/investing/052115/how-why-google-glass-failed.asp.

51. Betters, "Google Glass."

52. McGee, Matt. "Google Shuts Down Explorer Program, Reorganizes Glass Project." Glass Almanac, 2015. http://glassalmanac.com/google-shuts-explorer-program-reorganizes-glass-project/6861/.

53. Betters, "Google Glass."

54. Harris, Blake J. *The History of the Future: Oculus, Facebook, and the Revolution That Swept Virtual Reality*. HarperCollins, 2019.

55. "Oculus Rift: Step into the Game by Oculus." Kickstarter, 2012–2016. https://www.kickstarter.com/projects/1523379957/oculus-rift-step-into-the-game.

56. Facebook. "Facebook to Acquire Oculus." March 25, 2014. https://about.fb.com/news/2014/03/facebook-to-acquire-oculus/.

57. Harris, "The History of the Future."

58. Iqbal, Mansoor. "Pokémon GO Revenue and Usage Statistics (2020)." Business of Apps, March 8, 2021. https://www.businessofapps.com/data/pokemon-go-statistics/.

59. Templeman, Mike. "21 Pokemon Go Marketing Tactics You Have to Try." Entrepreneur Media, August 8, 2016. https://www.entrepreneur.com/article/279736.

60. Brainbridge. "From 1G to 5G: A Brief History of the Evolution of Mobile Standards." https://www.mcmc.gov.my/skmmgovmy /media/General/pdf/The-National-5G-Task-Force-Report.pdf.

61. Tibken, Shara. "Apple Becomes a Trillion-Dollar Company." CNET, August 3, 2018. https://www.cnet.com/news/apple-becomes-a-trillion-dollar-company/.

62. Thacker, C., E. McCreight, B. Lampson, R. Sproull, and D. Boggs. "Alto: A Personal Computer." In *Computer Structures: Principles and Examples*. 2nd edition. McGraw-Hill, 1981.

63. Berlin, Leslie. "The 1970s Xerox Conference That Predicted the Future of Work." Wired, December 27, 2017. https://www.wired.com/story/the-1970s-conference-that-predicted-the-future-of-work/.

64. Mark, Jerome A. "Technological Change and Employment." U.S. Bureau of Labor Statistics, 1987. https://stats.bls.gov /opub/mlr/1987/04/art3full.pdf.

65. Mark, "Technological Change."

66. Andrews, T. L. "Robots Won't Take Your Job—They'll Help Make Room for Meaningful Work Instead." Quartz, March 15, 2017. https://qz.com/932417/robots-wont-take-your-job-theyll-help-make-room-for-meaningful-work-instead/.

67. Diamandis, P. H., and S. Kotler. *The Future Is Faster Than You Think: How Converging Technologies Are Transforming Business, Industries, and Our Lives*. Simon & Schuster, p. 228–229.

68. Wilson, H. J., and P. R. Daugherty. "Collaborative Intelligence: Humans and AI Are Joining Forces." *Harvard Business Review,* July–August 2018. https://hbr.org/2018/07/collaborative-intelligence-humans-and-ai-are-joining-forces.

69. Diamandis and Kotler, *The Future Is Fast,* p. 229.

70. Alsop, Thomas. "Virtual Reality (VR)—Statistics and Facts." Statista, March 22, 2021. https://www.statista.com/topics/2532/ virtual-reality-vr/.

71. Statista. "Number of Virtual Reality (VR) and Augmented Reality (AR) Users in the United States from 2017 to 2022."

https://www.statista.com/statistics/1017008/united-states-vr-ar-users/.

72. Marilisaraccoglobal. "Is Generation Z Glued to Technology? It's Not an Addiction; It's an Extension of Themselves." Global News (Canada), June 19, 2018. https://globalnews.ca/news/4253835/generation-z-technology-addiction/.

73. Marilisaraccoglobal, "Is Generation Z Glued to Technology?"

74. Cleveland Clinic. "Text Neck: Is Smartphone Use Causing Your Neck Pain?" October 19, 2020. https://health.clevelandclinic.org/text-neck-is-smartphone-use-causing-your-neck-pain/.

75. Cleveland Clinic, "Text Neck."

76. Asurion, "Americans Check Their Phones 96 Times a Day." Cision US Inc., November 21, 2019. https://www.prnewswire.com/news-releases/americans-check-their-phones-96-times-a-day-300962643.html.

77. Christakis, Angela. "The Dangers of Distracted Parenting." *The Atlantic,* July–August 2018. https://www.theatlantic.com/magazine/archive/2018/07/the-dangers-of-distracted-parenting/561752/.

78. Haynes, Trevor. "Dopamine, Smartphones and You: A Battle for Your Time." Harvard University: The Graduate School for Arts & Sciences, May 1, 2018. http://sitn.hms.harvard.edu/flash/2018/dopamine-smartphones-battle-time.

79. Haynes, "Dopamine, Smartphones and You."

80. Newport, Cal. "On Digital Minimalism—Study Hacks." December 18, 2016. https://www.calnewport.com/blog/2016/12/18/on-digital-minimalism/.

81. Varghese, Daniel. "Can a Dumb Phone Fix Your Smartphone Addiction?" GQ, January 23, 2020. https://www.gq.com/story/light-phone-2-review.

82. McSpadden, Kevin. "You Now Have a Shorter Attention Span Than a Goldfish." Time, May 14, 2015. https://time.com/3858309/attention-spans-goldfish/.

83. McSpadden, "You Now Have a Shorter Attention Span."

84. Marilisaraccoglobal, "Is Generation Z Glued to Technology?"

85. Vogels, Emily A. "Millennials Stand Out for Their Technology Use." Pew Research Center, September 9, 2019. https://www.pewresearch.org/fact-tank/2019/09/09/us-generations-technology-use/.

86. Vincent, James. "Twitter Taught Microsoft's AI Chatbot to Be a Racist Asshole in Less than a Day." The Verge, March 24, 2016. https://www.theverge.com/2016/3/24/11297050/tay-microsoft-chatbot-racist.

87. Soul Machines. "Committed to Customer Success at Scale." 2021. https://www.soulmachines.com/products/soul-digital/.

88. O'Brien, Royal. "How Would You Keep 125 Million Gamers Playing Smoothly Online? Epic Games Shares Its Fortnite Story." Amazon Web Services, 2018. https://aws.amazon.com/blogs/gametech/epic-fortnite-all-in-on-aws-cloud/.

89. DeNisco Rayome, Alison. "6 industries That Are Using Blockchain to Drive Business Value Right No." TechRepublic, March 1, 2018. https://www.techrepublic.com/article/6-ways-companies-are-using-blockchain-to-drive-value-right-now/.

90. Kuo, Lily. "Imogen Heap Wants to Use Blockchain Technology to Revolutionize the Music Industry." Quartz, February 19, 2016. https://qz.com/620454/imogen-heap-wants-to-use-blockchain-technology-to-revolutionize-the-music-industry/.

91. Papagiannis, Helen. *Augmented Human: How Technology Is Shaping the New Reality.* O'Reilly Media, 2017.

92. Immerse.io. "Shell: Health and Safety Emergency Response Training." https://immerse.io/case_study/shell-health-and-safety-emergency-response-training/.

93. Avatar Dimensions, "Driving the Future of Immersive Video." https://www.avatar-dimension.com/.

94. Sourced from communication between Rosario B. Casas and the authors.

95. Ward, Tom. "The Mind Behind Minority Report Is Giving PowerPoint a Sci-fi Overhaul." Wired, December 3, 2019.

https://www.wired.co.uk/article/oblong-minority-report-john-underkoffler.

96. Garreau, Joel. "Washington as Seen in Hollywood's Crystal Ball." *The Washington Post,* June 21, 2002. https://www.washingtonpost.com/archive/lifestyle/2002/06/21/wash ington-as-seen-in-hollywoods-crystal-ball/9089c2d6-2ccb-477d-ac4d-0918ac968f3a/.

97. Rothkerch, Ian. "Will the Future Really Look Like 'Minority Report'?" Salon Media Group, Jully 10, 2002. https://web.archive.org/web/20110514220445/http://dir.salon.com/st ory/ent/movies/int/2002/07/10/underkoffler_belker/index.html.

98. Loughrey, Clarisse. "Minority Report: 6 Pedictions That Came True 15 Years On." Independent, June 25, 2017. https://www.independent.co.uk/arts-entertainment/films/features/minority-report-15th-anniversary-predictive-policing-gesture-based-computing-facial-and-optical-a7807666.html.

99. Arthur, Charles. "Why Minority Report Was Spot On." The Guardian, June 16, 2010. https://www.theguardian.com/technology/2010/jun/16/minority-report-technology-comes-true.

100. Shields, Jon. "Over 98% of Fortune 500 Companies Use Applicant Tracking Systems (ATS)." Jobscan, June 20, 2018. https://www.jobscan.co/blog/fortune-500-use-applicant-tracking-systems/.

101. OfficeTeam, "Survey: Six in 10 Companies Conduct Video Job Interviews." Cision US, August 30, 2012. https://www.prnewswire.com/news-releases/survey-six-in-10-companies-conduct-video-job-interviews-167973406.html.

102. Bayern, Macy. "86% of Companies Are Conducting Job Interviews via Video Conference." TechRepublic, April 30, 2020. https://www.techrepublic.com/article/86-of-companies-are-conducting-job-interviews-via-video-conference/.

103. Ozimek, Adam. "Economist Report: Future Workforce." UpWork Global, 2020. https://www.upwork.com/press/releases/economist-report-future-workforce.

104. Kimmorley, Sarah. "Stephen Hawking Made an Appearance at the Sydney Opera House via Hologram, and Had a Great Star Trek Exit." Business Insider Australia, April 26, 2015. https://www.businessinsider.com.au/stephen-hawking-has-made-an-appearance-at-the-sydney-opera-house-via-hologram-2015-4.

105. AT&T, "AT&T Brings 5G Technology to NBA Campus in Orlando." September 15, 2020. https://about.att.com/story/2020/nba_5g_hologram.html.

106. Young, Jabari. "The NBA Made It Through Its Pandemic Season, Now It Looks to 5G and VR in a Post-Covid World." CNBC, October 25, 2020. https://www.cnbc.com/2020/10/25/nba-new-revenue-exciting-future-5g-most-challenging-season.html.

107. Short, Matthew, and Shailee Samar. "Transforming Healthcare and Saving Lives with Extended Reality (XR)." Accenture's Technology Innovation Blog, November 28, 2017.

108. Talespin Reality Labs, Inc. "Copilot Platform: Virtual Human Training Technology Powered by Artificial Intelligence." https://www.talespin.com/copilot.

109. Sourced from communication between Cortney Harding and the authors.

110. Johnston, Lisa. "Stanley Black & Decker Taps AI for Workforce Training." Consumer Goods Technology, July 17, 2020. https://consumergoods.com/stanley-black-decker-taps-ai-workforce-training.

111. Stanley Black & Decker, Inc. "Stanley Black & Decker Partners with DeepHow to Deploy AI-Powered Technology." July 16, 2020. https://www.stanleyblackanddecker.com/article/stanley-black-decker-partners-deephow-deploy-ai-powered-technology.

112. Wesbecher, Jason. "How the New Emotional Workplace Affects Hiring, Retention and Culture." Entrepreneur, May 9, 2016. https://www.entrepreneur.com/article/272914.

113. Soul Machines. "Digital People Keep Employees Engaged in Corporate Learning and Development." 2020. https://www.soulmachines.com/2020/10/digital-people-keep-employees-engaged/.

114. Metropolitan Transportation Authority. "About Us." http://web.mta.info/mta/network.htm.

115. Lozé, Sébastien. "VR Perspectives Brings Inclusion and Diversity Through VR Training." Epic Games, August 11, 2020. https://www.unrealengine.com/en-US/spotlights/vr-perspectives-brings-inclusion-and-diversity-through-vr-training.

116. Ericsson. "Mobility Reports: 2019." Ericsson.com. https://www.ericsson.com/en/mobility-report/reports.

117. Sourced from communication between staff at Zebra Technologies and the authors.

118. Sourced from communication between Cortney Harding and the authors.

119. Sourced from communication between Nate Fender and the authors.

120. Sourced from communication between Sophia Moshasha and the authors.

121. Cockburn, I. M., R. Henderson, and S. Stern. "The Impact of Artificial Intelligence on Innovation." National Bureau of Economic Research, 2017. https://www.nber.org/papers/w24449.

122. Sourced from communication between Julie Smithson and the authors.

123. Sourced from communication between Elizabeth Baron and the authors.

124. Grasso, Catie. "How AI Is Transforming R&D (for the Better)." Data Iku, June 3, 2020. https://blog.dataiku.com/how-ai-is-transforming-rd-for-the-better.

125. Berruti, F., P. Nel, and R. Whiteman. "An Executive Primer on Artificial General Intelligence." McKinsey & Company, April 29, 2020. https://www.mckinsey.com/business-functions/operations/our-insights/an-executive-primer-on-artificial-general-intelligence#.

126. Gewirtz, David. "Google Duplex Beat the Turing Test: Are We Doomed?" ZDNet, May 14, 2018. https://www.zdnet.com/article/google-duplex-beat-the-turing-test-are-we-doomed/.

127. BBC. "Computer AI Passes Turing Test in 'World First.'" June 9, 2014. https://www.bbc.com/news/technology-27762088.

128. Sourced from communication between Sophia Moshasha and the authors.

129. Yao, Mariya. "Can Artificial Intelligence Make Anyone A Creative Artist?" TOPBOTS, 2017.

130. Funk Turkey. "NirvanA.I: I Made a Bot Write a Nirvana Song." YouTube video. June 15, 2020. https://www.youtube.com /watch?v=GogY7RQFFus.

131. Vincent, James. "Use This Cutting-Edge AI Text Generator to Write Stories, Poems, News Articles, and More." The Verge, May 13, 2019. https://www.theverge.com/tldr/2019/5/13/18617449/ai-text-generator-openai-gpt-2-small-model-talktotransformer.

132. Digital Engineering 24/7. "Deep Learning Meets 3D Modeling." January 10, 2020. https://www.digitalengineering247.com/article/ deep-learning-meets-3d-modeling/.

133. Snyder, Lily. "VR, IoT, and Manufacturing." June 4, 2018. https://lilyotron.blog/2018/06/04/vr-iot-and-manufacturing/.

134. NVIDIA Corporation. "Photorealistic Design Collaboration Using VR." https://www.nvidia.com/en-us/design-visualization /technologies/holodeck/.

135. Epic Games, Inc. "Validating Product Designs in Virtual Reality with MeshroomVR." August 21, 2020. https://www.unrealengine. com/en-US/spotlights/validating-product-designs-in-virtual-reality-with-meshroomvr.

136. Snyder, Lily. "Cincy Startup Week Recap: The Tech Frontier Series on Augmented and Virtual Reality." October 12, 2018. https://lilyotron.blog/2018/10/12/cincy-startup-week-recap-the-tech-frontier-series-on-augmented-and-virtual-reality/.

137. Sourced from communication between James Ashley and the authors.

138. Sourced from communication between Lisi Linares and the authors.

139. Garcia, Marisa. "KLM Launches Packing Tips Bot on Google Home." December 13, 2017, Phocuswire. https://www.phocuswire.com/KLM-launches-packing-tips-bot-on-Google-Home.

140. Capital One. "Eno Is Ready to Take Banking Conversations to the Next Level." October 24, 2017. https://www.capitalone.com/learn-grow/money-management/eno-chatbot-bankin g-conversations-next-level/.

141. Bloomberg Technology. "Meet AVA, Autodesk's New Virtual Assistant." YouTube video. June 1, 2018. https://www.youtube.com/watch?v=Ddl-tb566QQ.

142. Hackl, Cathy. "3 New Ways Artificial Intelligence Is Powering the Future of Marketing." Forbes, June 28, 2020. https://www.forbes.com/sites/cathyhackl/2020/06/28/3-new-ways-artificial-intelligence-is-powering-the-future-of-marketing/?sh=9b284691a96e.

143. Sourced from communication between Alan Smithson and the authors.

144. Hackl, Cathy. "5 Things Every CMO Needs to Know About How AR and VR Are Changing Marketing" Forbes, June 18, 2020. https://www.forbes.com/sites/cathyhackl/2020/06/18/5-things-every -cmo-needs-to-know-about-how-ar-and-vr-are-changing-marketing/?sh=65f5206b3b62.

145. Pogue, David. "Augmented Reality? Pogue Checks Out 7 of the First iPhone AR Apps." Yahoo!Finance, Octobeer 12, 2017. https://finance.yahoo.com/news/augmented-reality-pogue-checks-7-new-iphone-ar-apps-194000451.html.

146. Porsche. "Porsche Car Configurator." https://www.porsche.com/international/modelstart/.

147. The Porsche Newsroom. "New App Makes Three-Dimensional Vehicle Configuration Possible." May 22, 2019. https://newsroom.porsche.com/en/2019/digital/porsche-augmented-reality-visualizer-app-car-configuration-17619.html.

148. Sourced from communication between Dr. Joachim Scholz and the authors.

149. Sourced from communication between Alan Smithson and the authors.

150. Sourced from communication between Ashley Crowder and the authors.

151. Sourced from communication between Alex Goldberg and the authors.

152. Sourced from communication between Samantha G. Wolfe and the authors.

153. Sourced from communication between Navah Berg and the authors.

154. Alcántarah, Ann-Marie. "Ralph Lauren's Polo Player Goes Scannable and AR for the Holidays." *The Wall Street Journal,* November 18, 2020. https://www.wsj.com/articles/ralph-laurens-polo-player-goes-scannable-and-ar-for-the-holidays-11605697202.

155. Griffin, Keith. *Collaboration with the X Factor: How AI Is Transforming the Way We Work.* Cisco, 2019, p. 1–14. https://www.cisco.com/c/dam/global/en_uk/solutions/executive-perspectives/pdf/How-AI-is-transforming-the-way-we-work-Webex.pdf.

156. *Techopedia,* "Telepresence." https://www.techopedia.com/definition/14600/telepresence.

157. Microsoft. "Holoportation." https://www.microsoft.com/en-us/research/project/holoportation-3/.

158. Magic Leap. "Magic Leap: Spatial Computing for Enterprise." https://www.magicleap.com/.

159. Spatial. "How Work Should Be." https://spatial.io/.

160. Spatial, "How Work Should Be."

161. Microsoft. "What Is Dynamics 365." https://dynamics.microsoft.com/en-us/what-is-dynamics365/.

162. Microsoft. "Remote Assist—Microsoft Dynamics 365." https://dynamics.microsoft.com/en-us/mixed-reality/remote-assist/.

163. Microsoft, "Remote Assist."

164. Microsoft. "Product Roadmap—Microsoft Dynamics 365." https://dynamics.microsoft.com/en-us/roadmap/overview/.

165. Fernandez Guajardo, M., and L. Rutherford. "The Future of Work and the Next Computing Platform." Facebook, May 21, 2020. https://tech.fb.com/the-future-of-work-and-the-next-computing-platform/.

166. Lemonade. "The Secret Behind Lemonade's Claims." https://www.lemonade.com/claims.

167. Sourced from communication between Nate Fender and the authors.

168. Reisinger, Don. "How 5G Promises to Revolutionize Farming." Fortune, February 28, 2020. https://fortune.com/2020/02/28/5g-farming/.

169. Precision Hawk. "Drone Mapping and Analytics for Agriculture." https://www.precisionhawk.com/agriculture.

170. Francis, Sam. "John Deere Showcases Autonomous Electric Tractor and Other New Tech." Robotics & Automation News, November 19, 2019. https://roboticsandautomationnews.com/2019/11/19/john-deere-showcases-autonomous-electric-tractor-and-other-new-tech/26774/.

171. Alexander, Donovan. "9 Robots That Are Invading the Agriculture Industry." Interesting Engineering, November 13, 2018. https://interestingengineering.com/9-robots-that-are-invading-the-agriculture-industry.

172. Ramirez, Vanessa Bates. "Europe's Biggest Vertical Farm Will Be Powered by Wind and Planted by Robots." Singularity Hub. December 11, 2020. https://singularityhub.com/2020/12/11/europes-biggest-vertical-farm-will-be-powered-by-wind-and-planted-by-robots/.

173. Sourced from communication between James Ashley and the authors.

174. Bensley-Nettheim, Tili. "Bricklayers Meet Augmented Reality." Australian Design Review, April 14, 2020. https://www.australiandesignreview.com/architecture/bricklayers-meet-augmented-reality/.

242 · CATHY HACKL AND JOHN BUZZELL

175. Trimble Field Technology. "Your Data. Your Work Site. Together at Last." https://fieldtech.trimble.com/en/products/mixed-reality-visualization.

176. Bousquin, Joe. "The Future of Construction and 5G." Microdesk. https://www.microdesk.com/articles/the-future-of-construction-and-5g/.

177. CribMaster. "Take Control of Indirect Materials with CribMaster Inventory Management Solutions." https://www.cribmaster.com/solutions.

178. Bensley-Nettheim, "Bricklayers Meet Augmented Reality."

179. Autodesk. "Generative Design for Manufacturing with Fusion 360." https://www.autodesk.com/solutions/generative-design/manufacturing.

180. Autodesk. "Designing and Manufacturing to Break Speed Records." https://www.autodesk.com/campaigns/generative-design/lightning-motorcycles.

181. Bellamy, Woodrow, III. "Airlines Are Increasingly Connecting Artificial Intelligence to Their MRO Strategies." Avionics International, June 2019. http://interactive.aviationtoday.com/avionicsmagazine/june-2019/airlines-are-increasingly-connecting-artificial-intelligence-to-their-mro-strategies/.

182. Convrad, Thomas. "Toyota Evaluates Vehicle Ergonomics Utilizing VR and Unreal Engine." Epic Games, April 6, 2020. https://www.unrealengine.com/en-US/spotlights/toyota-evaluates-vehicle-ergonomics-utilizing-vr-and-unreal-engine.

183. BMW. "Innovation & Technology: A New Take on Vehicle Development." November 18, 2020. https://www.bmw.com/en/events/nextgen/global-collaboration.html.

184. Sloan, Keef. "Air Canada Uses VR to Showcase Its Top-Flight Business Class Service." Epic Games, December 3, 2019. https://www.unrealengine.com/en-US/spotlights/air-canada-uses-vr-to-showcase-its-top-flight-business-class-service.

185. Blackman, James. "VW and BMW Raise Industrial 5G Stakes – How German Car Giants Are Tooling Up for Industry 4.0." Enterprise

Insights, February 10, 2020. https://enterpriseiotinsights.com/20200210/channels/fundamentals/vw-and-bmw-raise-industrial-5g-stakes.

186. Jacobsen, Jacob. "14th FTW Innovation Flight Augments Pilot Training Through VR Technology." U.S. Air Force, February 14, 2020. https://www.af.mil/News/Article-Display/Article/2084928/14th-ftw-innovation-flight-augments-pilot-training-through-vr-technology/.

.187 Foundry 45. "Delta Air Lines Ramps Up Training With VR." https://foundry45.com/vr-case-studies/delta-air-lines-vr-training-experience/.

188. Carlton, Bobby. "Mercedes-Benz Looks to Replace Owner's Manual with AR App." VRScout, May 9, 2018. https://vrscout.com/news/mercedes-benz-ar-owners-manual/.

189. HPCWire. "AI Enters the Front Lines of National Defense and Security." July 29, 2019. https://www.hpcwire.com/2019/07/29/ai-enters-the-front-lines-of-national-defense-and-security/.

190. Librestream. "Onsight Connect Software." https://librestream.com/products/onsight-connect/.

191. U.S. Army CCDC Army Research Laboratory Public Affairs. "Augmented Reality Dog Goggles Could Help Protect Soldiers." October 6, 2020. https://www.army.mil/article/239705.

192. Sourced from communication between Tom Symonds and the authors.

193. Sourced from communication between Justin Parry and the authors.

194. Sourced from communication between Dr. Joachim Scholz and the authors.

195. Sourced from communication between Dr. Micah Shippee and the authors.

196. Sourced from communication between Roger Spitz and the authors.

197. Sourced from communication between Roger Spitz and the authors.

198. Sourced from communication between Dr. Micah Shippee and the authors.

199. Barton, Gina. "Why Your Netflix Thumbnails Don't Look Like Mine: A Thumbnail Is Worth a Thousand Words." Vox Media, November 21, 2018. https://www.vox.com/2018/11/21/18106394/ why-your-netflix-thumbnail-coverart-changes.

200. Wright, H., and G. Nelson. *Tomorrow's House. A Complete Guide for the Homebuilder.* Simon & Schuster, 1945.

201. Heaney, David. "Disney 'Basically Built A Multiplayer VR Filmmaking Game' to Direct the Lion King." Upload VR Media, April 29, 2019. https://uploadvr.com/the-lion-king-directed-in-vr/.

202. Farris, Jeff. "Forging New Paths for Filmmakers on 'The Mandalorian.'" Epic Games, February 20, 2020. https://www.unrealengine.com/en-US/blog/forging-new-paths-for-filmmakers-on-the-mandalorian.

203. Doubleeye.co. "A Live Interactive Virtual Reality Theater Performance." https://doubleeye.co/pandora.

204. La Biennale di Venezia. "Finding Pandora X: Venice VR Expanded." https://www.labiennale.org/en/cinema/2020/venice-vr-expanded/finding-pandora-x.

205. "Virtual Performance by Jean Michael Jarre for New Year's Eve 2021." Cultural Services French Embassy in the United States. https://frenchculture.org/events/12724-jean-michel-jarre-new-years-eve-2021.

206. Chan, Connie. "Shopatainment: Video Shopping as Entertainment." Andreessen Horowitz, December 14, 2020. https://a16z.com/2020/12/14/shopatainment/.

207. Shea, Cam. "The Games Industry on What Gaming Might Be Like in 2030." IGN, June 24, 2020. https://www.ign.com/articles/the-games-industry-on-what-gaming-might-be-like-in-2030.

208. Shea, "The Games Industry."

209. Ingham, Tim. "Sure, Streaming's Transformed the Music Business. But What's Next?" Rolling Stone, November 18, 2019. https://www.rollingstone.com/pro/news/streaming-transformed-music-business-whats-next-914029/.

210. Ingham, "Sure, Streaming's Transformed the Music Business."

211. Sourced from communication between Alex Coulombe and the authors.

212. Sourced from communication between Alex Coulombe and the authors.

213. Fidelity Center for Applied Technology. "Fidelity Labs: StockCity for Oculus Rift." YouTube video. November 18, 2014. https://www.youtube.com/watch?v=YQ2-8_2Vwpw.

214. Baker, Brandon, Matthew Carroll, Jaime Perry, and Bobby Tamburrino. "Using Oculus Rift and Virtual Reality to Visualize Data on Salesforce." Salesforce.com. https://www.salesforce.com/video/192746/.

215. CGS. "5 Augmented Reality Use Cases in the Workplace for Financial Services." August 18, 2020. https://www.cgsinc.com/blog/5-augmented-reality-use-cases-workplace-financial-services.

216. Phaneuf, Alicia. "Artificial Intelligence in Financial Services: Applications and Benefits of AI in Finance." Business Insider, September 9, 2020. https://www.businessinsider.com/ai-in-finance.

217. Kelley, Bruce. "Council Post: 5G in Financial Services: Evolution, Not Revolution." Forbes, September 10, 2020. https://www.forbes.com/sites/forbestechcouncil/2020/09/10/5g-in-financial-services-evolution-not-revolution/?sh=217633811dc0.

218. Sherman, Emily. "Guide to Eno: Account Monitoring and Virtual Card Numbers." CreditCards.com, January 3, 2020. https://www.creditcards.com/credit-card-news/capital-one-eno/.

219. Phillips, Michael, Jack Greenhalgh, Helen Marsden, and Ioulios Palamaras. "Detection of Malignant Melanoma Using Artificial Intelligence: An Observational Study of Diagnostic Accuracy." December 31, 2019. National Center for Biotechnology Information.

Dermatology Practical & Conceptual 10, no. 1 (2020): e2020011. https://www.ncbi.nlm.nih.gov/pmc/articles/PMC6936633/.

220. Stanford Medicine. "Virtual Reality System Helps Surgeons, Reassures Patients." https://medicalgiving.stanford.edu/news/virtual-reality-system-helps-surgeons-reassures-patients.html.

221. Pourmand, A., S. Davis, A. Marchak, T. Whiteside, and N. Sikka. "Virtual Reality as a Clinical Tool for Pain Management." *Current Pain and Headache Reports* 22, no. 8 (June 15, 2018): p. 53. doi: 10.1007/s11916-018-0708-2.

222. Gupta, A., K. Scott, and M. Dukewich. "Innovative Technology Using Virtual Reality in the Treatment of Pain: Does It Reduce Pain via Distraction, or Is There More to It?" *Pain Medicine* 19 (2018): p. 151–159. doi: 10.1093/pm/pnx109.

223. Hackl, Cathy. "What Is Volumetric Video and Why It Matters to the Enterprise." Forbes, September 27, 2020. https://www.forbes.com /sites/cathyhackl/2020/09/27/what-is-volumetric-video--why-it-matters-to-the-enterprise.

224. The University of British Columbia. "Volumetric Capture in Medical Training." Emerging Media Lab. http://eml.ubc.ca /projects/medical-volumetric-video/.

225. Schwartz, Peter. "Dr. Kai-Fu Lee on Why AI Redefines What It Means to Be Human." Salesforce.com. 2018.

226. Sourced from communication between Portico founders and the authors.

227. Houzen. "Invest in Highly Rentable Home—Entirely Online." https://houzen.co.uk/.

228. IBM. "INM Tririga." https://www.ibm.com/products/tririga.

229. GeoPhy. "Neighborhoods." https://geophy.com/neighborhoods/.

230. Matterport. "The Standard for 3D Space Capture and Collaboration." https://matterport.com.

231. Hover. "Eight Photos, Endless Possibilities." https://hover.to/.

232. Hooper, Adam. "How Will Blckchain and 5G Impact the Multifamily Sector." Multifamily Executive, September 5, 2019. https://www.multifamilyexecutive.com/technology/how-will-blockchain-and-5g-impact-the-multifamily-sector_o.

233. Sutevski, Dragan. "How Machine Learning Can Transform Sales." Entrepreneurship in a Box. https://www.entrepreneurshipinabox.com/21862/how-machine-learning-can-transform-sales.

234. Businesswire. "Sports – $614 Billion Global Market Opportunities and Strategies to 2022 – ResearchAndMarkets.com." May 14, 2019. https://www.businesswire.com/news/home/20190514005472/en/Sports---614-Billion-Global-Market-Opportunities.

235. Menear, Harry. "Smart Stadiums: The Future of Live Sports Entertainment." Technology, November 1, 2020. https://www.technologymagazine.com/cloud-and-cybersecurity/smart-stadiums-future-live-sports-entertainment.

236. Penfold, Andy. "3 Ways AI Cameras Can Improve Fan Experience in Sports Stadiums." Security and Safety Things, February 6, 2020. https://www.securityandsafetythings.com/insights/ai-improve-fan-experience-sports-stadiums.

237. Sprigg, Sam. "Sports Gambling Group Entain Partners with Verizon Media to Develop Immersive VR and AR Experiences for Live Sports Viewing and Betting." Auganix, December 29, 2020. https://www.auganix.org/sports-gambling-group-entain-partners-with-verizon-media-to-develop-immersive-vr-and-ar-experiences-for-live-sports-viewing-and-betting/.

238. Newberry, Joe. "How to Watch Sports Events in VR." Culture, November 27, 2020. https://thesportsdaily.com/2020/11/27/how-to-watch-sports-events-in-vr/.

239. Scott-Briggs, Angela. "The Advantages of Augmented Reality in Sports." TechBullion, March 21, 2020. https://techbullion.com/the-advantages-of-augmented-reality-in-sports.

240. Sourced from communication between Jason Yim and the authors.

241. Gulfstream Aerospace Corporation. "Gulfstream Reality Experiences at EBACE 2018." YouTube video. May 30, 2018. https://www.youtube.com/watch?v=HdYuwaN6XEg.

242. Foundry 45, "Delta Air Lines Ramps Up Training with VR."

243. Levine, Barry. "Here's How Marketing Research Is Looking Past Consumers and Connecting with Their Bodies." MarTech Today, October 5, 2016. https://martechtoday.com/heres-marketing-research-looking-past-consumers-connecting-bodies-191281.

244. Mendoza, N. F. "Data Privacy: What Consumers Want Businesses to Know." TechRepublic, February 19, 2020. https://www.techrepublic.com/article/data-privacy-what-consumers-want-businesses-to-know/.

245. Mendoza, "Data Privacy."

246. Ai Foundation. "About." https://aifoundation.com/about/.

247. Sourced from communication between Roger Spitz and the authors.

248. Deloitte. "Consumer 2020: Reading the Signs." Deloitte Global Services Limited, 2020, p. 1–26. https://www2.deloitte.com/ru/en/pages/consumer-business/articles/consumer-2020.html.

249. Deloitte, "Consumer 2020," p. 1–26.

250. Deloitte, "Consumer 2020," p. 11.

251. Deloitte, "Consumer 2020," p. 11.

252. Hudson, David L., Jr. "Free Speech or Censorship? Social Media Litigation Is a Hot Legal Battleground." American Bar Association Journal, April 1, 2019. https://www.abajournal.com/magazine/article/social-clashes-digital-free-speech.

253. Andrews, Robert. "Second Life Rocks (Literally)." Wired, August 15, 2006. https://www.wired.com/2006/08/second-life-rocks-literally/.

254. Webster, Andrew. "More Than 12 Million People Attended Travis Scott's Fortnite Concert." The Verge, April 23, 2020.

https://www.theverge.com/2020/4/23/21233946/travis-scott-fortnite-concert-astronomical-record-breaking-player-count.

255. Hackl, Cathy. "Toward the Metaverse: What Fortnite's Latest Concert Tells Us About the Future of Virtual Presence." LinkedIn, May 14, 2020. https://www.linkedin.com/pulse/toward-metaverse-what-fortnites-latest-concert-tells-us-cathy-hackl.

256. Hackl, Cathy. "Marketing to Robots: Why CMOs Need to Start Thinking About Business to Robot to Consumer (B2R2C)." Forbes, June 14, 2020. https://www.forbes.com/sites/cathyhackl/2020/06/14/marketing-to-robots-why-cmos-need-to-start-thinking-about-business-to-robot-to-consumer-b2r2c/.

257. Kay, Jeremy. "VR Writ Large Over Cannes Marché NEXT Programme." ScreenDaily, April 20, 2016. https://www.screendaily.com/cannes-news/vr-writ-large-over-cannes-marche-next-programme-/5102820.article.

258. Feltham, Jamie. "Is VR Dead? The Arguments for and Against the Industry's Demise." UploadVR Media, February 14, 2019. https://uploadvr.com/is-vr-dead/.

259. Sanders, James. "How 5G Will Affect Augmented Reality and Virtual Reality." ZDNet, October 2, 2019. https://www.zdnet.com/article/how-5g-will-affect-augmented-reality-and-virtual-reality/.

260. Sanders, "How 5G Will Affect Augmented Reality and Virtual Reality."

261. Kelly, Kevin. "AR Will Spark the Next Big Tech Platform—Call It Mirrorworld." Wired, February 12, 2019. https://www.wired.com/story/mirrorworld-ar-next-big-tech-platform/.

262. Cohen, Maor. "How the Coronavirus Crisis Will Shape the Future of Virtual Reality." Forbes, May 21, 2020. https://www.forbes.com/sites/columbiabusinessschool/2020/05/21/how-coronavirus-crisis-will-shape-future-of-virtual-reality/.

263. Businesswire. "COVID-19 Impact and Recovery Analysis—Global Augmented Reality (AR) and Virtual Reality (VR) Market 2020–2024." June 26, 2020. https://www.businesswire.com/news/home/20200626005010/en/COVID-19-Impact-Recovery-Analysis--Global-Augmented-Reality.

264. Virtual Reality World Tec. "How VR Training Can Help Leaders Unlock the True Value of Their Workforce." September 27, 2019. https://vrworldtech.com/2019/09/27/how-vr-training-can-help-leaders-unlock-the-true-value-of-their-workforce/.

265. Sourced from communication between Justin Parry and the authors.

266. AR Insider. "What's the Next Dimension of Spatial Computing?" May 9, 2019. https://arinsider.co/2019/05/09/whats-the-next-dimension-of-spatial-computing/.

267. Sculley, John. "John Sculley Quotes." BrainyQuote. https://www.brainyquote.com/quotes/john_sculley_130757.

268. Oracle. "What Is CX?" https://www.oracle.com/cx/what-is-cx/.

269. Whiting, Kate. "These Are the Top 10 Job Skills of Tomorrow—and How Long It Takes to Learn Them." World Economic Forum, October 21, 2020. https://www.weforum.org/agenda/2020/10/top-10-work-skills-of-tomorrow-how-long-it-takes-to-learn-them/.

270. D'Onfro, Jillian. "Jeff Bezos' Brilliant Advice for Anyone Running a Business." Business Insider, January 31, 2015. https://www.businessinsider.com/jeff-bezos-brilliant-advice-for-anyone-running-a-business-2015-1.

271. Quote Investigator. "I Have Gotten a Lot of Results! I Know Several Thousand Things That Won't Work." https://quoteinvestigator.com/2012/07/31/edison-lot-results/#:~:text=I've%20discovered%20ten%20thousand,700%20ways%20will%20not%20work.

About the Authors

Cathy Hackl is a globally recognized tech futurist and business executive, speaker, and media personality specializing in AR, VR, spatial computing, and the Metaverse. She's one of LinkedIn's top technology voices, and BigThink named her one of the top ten most influential women in tech in 2020. She's been called the CEO's business guide to the Metaverse and was included in the prestigious Thinkers50 Radar list of the 30 management thinkers most likely to shape the future of how global organizations are managed and led. She founded the Futures Intelligence Group, an emerging-technology consulting firm that helps brands enter the Metaverse through strategic foresight and next-gen actionable strategies. Hackl has worked with some of the biggest names in tech, including Amazon Web Services (AWS), Magic Leap, and HTC VIVE.

She is a sought-after keynote speaker and has spoken at CES, SXSW, Comic-Con, Adobe Summit, Harvard Business School, MIT, Facebook, Twitter, Aspen Institute, In-Q-Tel, US Navy, SDA Bocconi, IE, and Singularity University, and across the globe.

John Buzzell is an award-winning leader in emerging technology who's created experiences across the last six major digital transformations, including augmented reality and virtual reality, mobile apps, videogames, websites, and more. Focused on technology for media and marketing, he's led innovative work with AT&T, Coca-Cola, Porsche, Cartoon Network, the NBA, NYC Transit, Stanley Black & Decker, Aflac, NBC, Time Warner, Discovery, and National Geographic. He founded the VR/AR Association's global committee for Marketing and Advertising. Today, he helps enterprise customers using Unreal Engine from Epic Games—leading customers through the next technology transition and into a multi-platform metaverse of real-time 3D. He's an active speaker as well, covering innovation topics like the metaverse, AR, VR, real-time 3D animation, experiential technology, digital strategy, and more.

Appearances include the Augmented World Expo, the Hollywood Professional Association, VRDC, Reuters XR USA, and M.I.T.

Made in the USA
Coppell, TX
20 January 2022

71960311R00144